WORKBOOK

FUTURE 3

English for Work, Life, and Academic Success

Second Edition

Series Consultants
Sarah Lynn
Ronna Magy
Federico Salas-Isnardi

Pearson

Future 3 Workbook
English for Work, Life, and Academic Success
Copyright © 2019 by Pearson Education, Inc.

Pearson Education, 221 River Street, Hoboken, NJ 07030 USA

Staff credits: The people who made up the *Future 3 Workbook* team, representing content development, design, manufacturing, marketing, multimedia, project management, publishing, rights management, and testing, are Pietro Alongi, Jennifer Castro, Dave Dickey, Gina DiLillo, Warren Fischbach, Pamela Fishman, Gosia Jaros-White, Joanna Konieczna, Michael Mone, Mary Perrotta Rich, Katarzyna Starzyńska-Kościuszko, Claire Van Poperin, Joseph Vella, Gabby Wu.

Text composition: Dataflow International
Cover design: EMC Design Ltd
Audio: CityVox

ISBN-13: 978-0-13-454762-6
ISBN-10: 0-13-454762-4

Printed in the United States of America

12 2022

CONTENTS

TO THE TEACHER

The *Future 3 Workbook* has 12-page units to complement what students have learned in the Student Book. Each Workbook unit follows the lesson order of the Student Book and provides supplemental practice in vocabulary, life skills, listening, grammar, reading, and writing. Students can complete the exercises outside the classroom as homework or during class time to extend instruction.

The Workbook audio includes the readings from the Workbook so students can become more fluent readers.

UNIT STRUCTURE

Vocabulary

Practice focuses on the vocabulary presented on the first spread of the unit. Typical activities are word and sentence completion, labeling, and categorizing. Some lessons include sentence writing to reinforce the lesson's vocabulary, and some lessons include personalized exercises.

Grammar

Grammar is practiced in contextualized exercises that include sentence completion, sentence writing, sentence scrambles, matching, and multiple choice. Some lessons also include vocabulary exercises to reinforce the new vocabulary taught in the lesson. Some lessons include personalized activities.

Workplace, Life, and Community Skills

In the second edition, the Life Skills lesson has been revised to focus on workplace, life, and community skills and to develop the real-life language and civic literacy skills required today. Lessons integrate and contextualize workplace content. In addition, every lesson includes practice with digital skills on a mobile device.

Writing

In the second edition, a cumulative writing lesson has been added to every unit. This new lesson requires students to synthesize and apply their learning in a written outcome. Through a highly scaffolded approach, students begin by analyzing writing models before planning and finally producing written work of their own.

Reading

All reading lessons have new, information-rich texts and a revised pedagogical approach in line with the CCR and ELP standards and the NRS descriptors. These informational texts are level appropriate, use high-frequency vocabulary, and focus on interpretation of graphic information. The readings build students' knowledge and develop their higher-order reading skills by teaching citation of evidence, summarizing, and interpretation of complex information from a variety of text formats.

Soft Skills at Work

Future has further enhanced its development of workplace skills by adding a Soft Skills at Work lesson to each unit. Soft skills are the critical interpersonal communication skills needed to succeed in any workplace. Students begin each lesson by discussing a common challenge in the workplace. Then, while applying the lesson-focused soft skill, they work to find socially appropriate solutions to the problem.

ADDITIONAL RESOURCES

At the back of the Workbook, you will find:
- My Soft Skills Log
- Writing Checklist
- Answer Key

ORIENTATION

The Workbook, like the Student Book, includes an orientation for students. Before the students use the Workbook for the first time, direct them to To the Student on the next page. Go through the questions and tips with the students and answer any questions they may have so they can get the most out of using the Workbook.

LEARN ABOUT YOUR BOOK

A **Look in the back of your book. Write the page number for this section.**

My Soft Skills Log ___   Answer Key ___

B **Look at page 155. Find _Answers will vary._ What does _Answers will vary_ mean?**

C **Where is the audio?**

D **Look at page 5. What does ▶ mean?**

TIPS FOR USING THE AUDIO

Read the tips for using the audio.

- In the Reading lessons, use the audio to help you understand the articles.
- When listening for details, use the pause button so you can have more time to write and find the information you need.
- After you finish the unit, play the audio again and review the readings.
- Also, for more listening practice, listen to the readings when you are in the car or on the bus.

WRITING TIPS

Read the writing tips.

- Start sentences with a capital letter.
- End statements with a period (.).
- End questions with a question mark (?).

For example:

My name is Jack.

What's your name?

Use the Writing Checklist in the back of your book to check your writing.

Lesson 1: Vocabulary

A Match the countries on the map with their names. Write the letters.

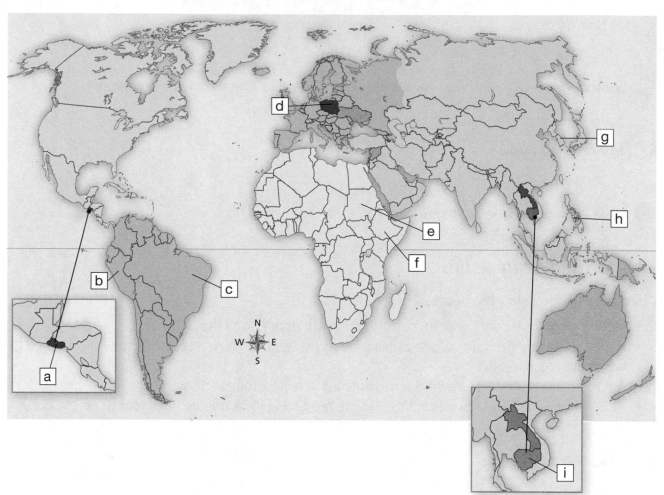

_____ **1.** Cambodia   _____ **2.** South Korea   _____ **3.** Poland

_____ **4.** Peru   _____ **5.** Sudan   _____ **6.** Ethiopia

_____ **7.** El Salvador   _____ **8.** Philippines   _____ **9.** Brazil

B Look at the country names in the box. Write the name of each country next to the continent where it is located.

Ukraine	Ecuador	Poland	Nigeria
Colombia	the Philippines	Algeria	Vietnam
Somalia	Norway	Argentina	Japan

South America: _____ _____ _____

Europe: _____ _____ _____

Asia: _____ _____ _____

Africa: _____ _____ _____

C Match the countries with the languages.

1. Cambodia   _e_   **a.** Spanish

2. Laos   ___   **b.** Ukrainian

3. South Korea   ___   **c.** Lao

4. the Philippines   ___   **d.** Korean

5. Colombia   ___   **e.** Khmer (Cambodian)

6. Ukraine   ___   **f.** Filipino

7. China   ___   **g.** Portuguese

8. Poland   ___   **h.** Mandarin

9. Brazil   ___   **i.** Polish

D WRITE ABOUT IT. What country would you like to visit? Why? Write three sentences.

I would like to visit South Korea because I love Korean barbecue.

_____

_____

_____

_____

Lessons 2 & 3: Grammar

A Complete the sentences. Use the simple present form of the verbs in parentheses. Use contractions for the negative sentences.

1. Edgar _____doesn't live_____ in Los Angeles.
   (not / live)

2. Mimi and Eric _____ a picnic in the park every Sunday.
   (have)

3. Sue _____ basketball.
   (not / play)

4. Lin _____ classes on Tuesdays.
   (have)

5. Roberto and Carlos _____ the games.
   (not / watch)

6. Nicole and Amy _____ in Dallas.
   (live)

7. The beach _____ Teresa of Brazil.
   (remind)

8. My family _____ in the United States.
   (not / live)

B Write questions. Use the simple present.

1. (do / you / what / in your free time)
   What do you do in your free time?

2. (for a walk / she / go / how often)
   _____

3. (live / they / where / now)
   _____

4. (live / in Los Angeles / they)
   _____

5. (American football / play / he)
   _____

Lesson 4: Reading

A ▶ Listen and read.

THE CHINESE COMMUNITY IN SAN FRANCISCO

Chinese Americans have lived in San Francisco for a long time. The first **immigrants** arrived in the 1840s. They worked in mines and on farms. They made
5 clothes and helped to build the railroads. These workers brought new foods and goods to California.

The first Chinese Americans lived and worked in an area now called Chinatown. It
10 is the oldest Chinese area in the U.S. The area is filled with shops and restaurants. Many people also live there. Visitors to the city enjoy eating Chinese food and shopping for gifts. The Chinese New Year festival in
15 this area is the largest in America. On Friday evenings, there are free music **performances** and games for children.

San Francisco is famous for its Chinese food. American workers in the 1850s ate it
20 because it was cheap and **delicious**. Restaurants in the city began to make new dishes, like chop suey, a dish with different types of meat, eggs, vegetables, and rice. The food was sweet and fried. This was how Americans liked it. Today, many people in the city still eat Chinese food every week.

People from Chinese families have held some of San Francisco's most important jobs. They have been mayor of
25 the city and chief of police. Others have been famous. Bruce Lee was born in the city in 1940. His movies made martial arts popular across the world. Amy Tan writes about the lives of Chinese families in America. Millions of people read her book *The Joy Luck Club*.

The Chinese community has had a positive effect on the culture of San Francisco. It would not be the same without it.

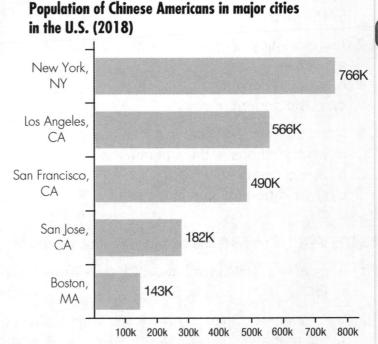

Population of Chinese Americans in major cities in the U.S. (2018)

New York, NY — 766K
Los Angeles, CA — 566K
San Francisco, CA — 490K
San Jose, CA — 182K
Boston, MA — 143K

(100k 200k 300k 400k 500k 600k 700k 800k)

B DEVELOP YOUR ACADEMIC SKILLS. Read the Academic Skill. Circle the correct answer.

The main idea of the text is that Chinese Americans _____.
   a. lived in cities across the United States
   b. were good at many different jobs
   c. helped shape San Francisco

> **Academic Skill:**
> **Understanding the main idea**
>
> The main idea is the most important idea in an article. The main idea is often found in the first paragraph.

C IDENTIFY. What is the main idea of the third paragraph?

Chinese food in America _____.
   a. was not eaten by Americans
   b. is still very popular
   c. tastes the same as food in China

D CITE EVIDENCE. Complete the sentences. Where is the information? Write the line number.

Lines

1. Chinese people have lived in San Francisco for more than _____.
   a. 200 years
   b. 250 years
   c. 150 years

   _____

2. Tourists enjoy Chinatown for its _____.
   a. history
   b. food and culture
   c. music performances

   _____

3. Many Chinese Americans in San Francisco _____.
   a. work in shops and restaurants
   b. like to create new food
   c. have important jobs in the city

   _____

E INTERPRET. Complete the sentences about the chart.

1. Two cities in California have a Chinese American population that is higher than _____.
   a. 450k   b. 500k   c. 550k

2. The number of Chinese Americans living in San Jose is _____ that in Boston.
   a. higher than   b. lower than   c. the same as

3. The number of Chinese Americans living in New York is _____ higher than that in Los Angeles.
   a. 150k   b. 180k   c. 200k

F INTERPRET VOCABULARY. Complete the sentences.

1. The word *immigrants* in line 3 means _____.
   a. people who come to live in a new country
   b. people who work as builders

2. The word *performances* in line 17 means _____.
   a. shows   b. classes

3. The word *delicious* in line 20 means _____.
   a. healthy   b. tasty

G SUMMARIZE. What are the most important ideas in the article? Write three sentences.

_____

_____

_____

Lessons 5 & 6: Grammar

A Unscramble the sentences. More than one answer is sometimes possible.

1. (rarely / go / to the movies / I)

   I rarely go to the movies.

2. (to the park / always / Tim / on Mondays / goes)

   _____

3. (after school / never / basketball / my sister / plays)

   _____

4. (we / on the weekend / to the supermarket / usually / go)

   _____

5. (in the morning / I / exercises / do / sometimes)

   _____

B Rewrite the sentences. Use the adverbs of frequency in parentheses.

1. I eat a big breakfast before I go to work. **(always)**

   I always eat a big breakfast before I go to work.

2. I go to the library after school. **(usually)**

   _____

3. My children shop at the mall on Sundays. **(often)**

   _____

4. She meets her friends at a café after work. **(sometimes)**

   _____

5. I eat before I go to bed. **(never)**

   _____

C The sentences have errors. Correct the errors. Rewrite the sentences.

1. I go often to the pharmacy to pick up my medication.

_____

2. My wife goes always to the post office to buy stamps.

_____

3. My children play tennis on the weekend usually.

_____

4. Never we go to the hair salon during the week.

_____

5. I have a sandwich and fruit for lunch rarely.

_____

D Read the paragraph. Correct five more mistakes with adverbs of frequency.

Asha is from Somalia, but now she lives in Minnesota. She and her family ⌄*usually* eat ~~usually~~ dinner together. In Somalia, lunch always was the biggest meal, but in the United States, families don't have time for a long lunch. Asha fries her food usually. She and her family prefer lamb, but they always don't get it. Sometimes they have beef or chicken. They also often have bread with their meals. They finish the meal always with spicy sweet tea. In the United States, she is able to buy many kinds of vegetables. In Somalia, there weren't as many vegetables available so rarely they had them.

Lesson 7: Workplace, Life, and Community Skills

A Read the recipe. Circle the ingredients.

Chicken and Pasta Salad

You will need:
- ¼ pound of chicken meat
- 1 head of lettuce
- ½ pound of pasta (macaroni)
- 4 large tomatoes
- 1 tablespoon of vinegar
- 1 tablespoon of oil
- salt

1. Boil the pasta for 10 minutes until cooked.
2. Fry the chicken until cooked through, and cut into thin slices.
3. Wash the lettuce, and place the leaves in a large bowl.
4. Chop the tomatoes into small pieces.
5. Put the chicken, tomatoes, and pasta in the same bowl as the lettuce, and mix them together.
6. Sprinkle in some salt, and add the vinegar and oil, and mix all the ingredients.

B Complete the steps for how to make chicken and pasta salad.

1. Cook _____ in boiling water for 10 minutes.
   - **a.** 1 head of lettuce
   - **b.** ¼ pound of chicken meat
   - **c.** ½ pound of pasta

2. Cut the fried _____ into slices.
   - **a.** chicken
   - **b.** tomatoes
   - **c.** vinegar

3. Chop _____ into pieces.
   - **a.** 4 large tomatoes
   - **b.** ½ pound of pasta
   - **c.** 1 head of lettuce

4. Add the _____ last.
   - **a.** pasta
   - **b.** salt, vinegar, and oil
   - **c.** lettuce

C WRITE ABOUT IT. Look up a recipe for your favorite dish online. Write the ingredients and the steps for preparing it.

_____

_____

_____

_____

_____

_____

D Read the food storage guidelines. Then circle the correct answers.

What do you do with leftovers —foods you didn't finish?

Some types of foods, such as meat, poultry, and eggs can go bad quickly. If they have been left at room temperature longer than two hours, throw them out. Some exceptions to this rule are foods such as cookies, crackers, bread, and whole fruits. These can be stored at room temperature.

Whole roasts, hams, and turkeys should be sliced or cut into smaller pieces before storing them in the refrigerator or freezer. Turkey legs, wings, and thighs may be left whole. Refrigerate or freeze leftovers in containers. Wrap or cover the food.

REFRIGERATOR STORAGE AT 40°F OR BELOW

Cooked meat or poultry	3 to 4 days
Pizza	3 to 4 days
Lunch meat	3 to 5 days
Eggs, tuna, and macaroni salads	3 to 5 days

Foods stored longer may become unsafe to eat. Do not taste them.

FREEZER STORAGE AT 0°F OR BELOW

Cooked meat or poultry	3 to 4 weeks
Pizza	3 to 4 weeks
Fruits and vegetables	3 to 5 weeks

Salads made with mayonnaise do not freeze well.

Remember—when in doubt, throw it out!

1. You want to save a turkey leg. What should you do?

   a. Cut it up and put it on a plate in the refrigerator.

   b. Leave it whole, wrap it up, and put it in the refrigerator.

   c. Throw it away.

2. You made a pasta salad dish with mayonnaise. It was sitting out for two hours. What should you do?

   a. Cover it and put it in the refrigerator.

   b. Throw it away.

   c. Cover it and put it in the freezer.

3. You saved leftover pizza for six days in your refrigerator. What should you do?

   a. Heat it first, and then eat it.

   b. Eat it right away.

   c. Throw it away.

4. You can't remember how long some meat has been in your refrigerator. What should you do?

   a. Throw it away.

   b. Keep it and eat it soon.

   c. Put it in the freezer.

Lesson 8 & 9: Grammar

A Complete the sentences. Cross out the incorrect quantifier.

1. I tried **a little / ~~much~~** salsa at the food festival but it was very spicy.

2. Adults give children **a lot of / any** red pockets on Chinese New Year.

3. I didn't eat **a few / any** of the food at the Mayan Food Festival.

4. There wasn't **much / a little** cake left after the birthday party.

5. I ate **much / several** pieces of pineapple at the Pineapple Festival in Oaxaca.

B Complete the conversation. Cross out the incorrect quantifiers.

A: I want to make tortilla soup. How can I get a recipe for it? Should I buy a cookbook?

B: You don't have to buy **~~a few~~ / any** cookbooks. You can search for recipes on the internet. Just type in the name of a dish, and **a lot of / much** recipes will come up.

A: Oh, really? I usually don't find **any / some** good information on the internet. How do you do it?

B: I just type in the name of the food I want in the search bar. Be careful that you don't click on an advertisement. There are always **a lot of / a little** advertisements online.

A: Good idea. I'll do that. Tomorrow I'll spend **a few / some** time looking for recipes. Where can I use the internet? My computer isn't working right now.

B: There's an internet café on the corner with **several / any** computers.

C WRITE ABOUT IT. What are your favorite holiday foods? What do you eat a lot of? What don't you eat much of?

I always eat sweets on New Year's Eve.

_____

_____

_____

Lesson 10: Writing

A Read the Writing Skill. Which paragraphs have a topic sentence? Circle the correct answers.

a. I love going to the mall. Every Friday evening, I go to the mall with my friends. I usually get home at around 9.00 P.M.

b. I moved with my parents and three brothers. It is a very rural area. We like it a lot.

c. Marisa often goes to the park. She likes to walk her dog there. Sometimes she meets her friends there, and they go to a café after.

> **Writing Skill: Write a topic sentence**
>
> The topic sentence gives the main idea of a paragraph. It describes what the paragraph will be about. For example: (I really enjoy Chinese New Year.) Every year, I go with my friends to see the celebrations. Sometimes we set off firecrackers.

B Which sentence is the best topic sentence for this paragraph? Circle the topic sentences.

We moved from El Salvador. We stayed with our uncle for a month until we found our own house. There are lots of things to do here. We play basketball every day in the park near our house.

a. Our uncle is very helpful.

b. My sister and I moved to San Francisco in 2016.

c. I often miss my old home.

C Read the text. Correct five more errors.

moved
I ~~move~~ to New York from Brazil two years ago. The town I am from is very small, but New York is a very big city! I came here because my cousin live here. He working in a restaurant. He helped me get a job there, too. I like working there. The work are hard but my co-workers are very friendly. At first, I didn't have some friends. Now I have many friends. Always we go to the movies on Saturday nights.

Lesson 11: Soft Skills at Work

A UNDERSTAND. Complete the sentence. Circle the correct answer.

A person who is inclusive is someone who _____.
- **a.** talks a lot
- **b.** makes others feel like part of a group
- **c.** tells jokes about others

B IDENTIFY. Read the conversations at work. In which conversations are the people being inclusive? Check (✓) the conversations.

❑ **1. Sara:** Hi, Karla. Are you doing anything for lunch?

    Karla: Not really. I usually have lunch at my desk.

    Sara: I'm going to a new café with a few people from the office. Would you like to join us?

    Karla: Sure, that sounds great!

❑ **2. Cumar:** Hello. Are you new here?

    Aldo: Yes, I started a few days ago.

    Cumar: Welcome! My name is Cumar.

    Aldo: I'm Aldo. I'm from Portugal, and I moved to the U.S. a year ago.

    Cumar: Well, it's nice to meet you. If you have any problems, let me know. I always sit over there.

❑ **3. Anissa:** What do you think of the new supervisor?

    Van: Sam? I don't like him at all. Sometimes, he can be slow to reply to my emails.

❑ **4. Ali:** I love the tacos at this restaurant. What do you think of them?

    Linda: They're OK, but they're too big. There's a lot of meat! I prefer something lighter, like soup. What about you?

    Justin: I'm a vegetarian, so I usually have fried rice with beans when I come here.

C ANALYZE. Read the conversations in Exercise B again. What are the different ways the people are inclusive? Check (✓) the boxes.

❑   **a.** ask their opinions

❑   **b.** make new co-workers feel welcome

❑   **c.** complain about someone to other co-workers

❑   **d.** invite others to social events

Unit 2: Setting Goals

Lesson 1: Vocabulary

A Look at the pictures. Complete the sentences with the words in the box.

financial aid	a certificate	citizenship classes	a high school diploma

1. Ed is taking

_____.

2. Sofia is applying for

_____.

3. Christine is getting

_____.

4. Paul is getting

_____.

B Match the beginning of each sentence with its correct ending.

1. Donna is going to get   _b_   **a.** in college this year.

2. Zoltan will apply   ___   ~~b.~~ a degree in history.

3. Lucy wants to   ___   **c.** for financial aid this semester.

4. Derek will enroll   ___   **d.** for the semester.

5. Edgar is going to register   ___   **e.** get a promotion.

C What kind of goal does each person have? Circle the correct answers.

1. Fatima wants to earn a high school diploma.
   (a.) school goal   **b.** work goal   **c.** community goal

2. Shu-fen wants to earn a promotion.
   a. school goal   **b.** work goal   **c.** community goal

3. Christina wants experience as a volunteer at a food bank.
   a. school goal   **b.** work goal   **c.** community goal

4. Jee Min wants to earn a certificate in early childhood education.
   a. school goal   **b.** work goal   **c.** community goal

5. Alex wants to register for the semester.
   a. school goal   **b.** work goal   **c.** community goal

6. Dawit wants to clean up trash in his neighborhood.
   a. school goal   **b.** work goal   **c.** community goal

D WRITE ABOUT IT. What are your goals? Email a friend about a work, school, or community goal you would like to work on this year.

⊗ ⊖ ⊕

From:	Vanessa Ali
To:	David Kaya
Subject:	Hi!

Hi _____,

Thanks for your last email.

_____

_____

_____

_____

Lessons 2 & 3: Grammar

A Complete the sentences. Cross out the incorrect words.

1. Tom needs financial aid, or he ~~might~~ / won't be able to take classes in the fall.

2. Cassie **will / won't** apply for financial aid because she has saved enough money.

3. Omar **will / won't** volunteer at the community center because he likes to spend time there.

4. Trung **might / will** work at night next week, but she doesn't know yet.

5. Philip registered for classes this morning. He **will / won't** take three classes.

6. Sasha **might / won't** get his ASE certificate until next spring.

B Complete the conversations. Use *will*, *might*, or *won't*. Use contractions when possible.

1. **A:** Hey, Jeremy. Congratulations on getting your degree! Now that you've graduated,

   will you change jobs soon?

   B: I don't know. I _____.

2. **A:** I think I _____ register for the fall semester if I can get financial aid.

   B: You should definitely do that.

3. **A:** What _____ you study this semester?

   B: I don't know yet.

4. **A:** Are you going to study tonight?

   B: Yes, I _____. I have a quiz tomorrow.

5. **A:** Will you start classes in the fall?

   B: No, I _____. I'm waiting for the Spring semester.

6. **A:** Will you keep working?

   B: I'm not sure. I _____. I need to ask my boss if I can work part-time.

Lesson 4: Reading

A DEVELOP YOUR ACADEMIC SKILLS. Read the Academic Skill. Look at the picture and the title of the article. Circle the correct answer.

The topic of the article will be _____.
   a. how to develop a new product
   b. typical immigrant businesses
   c. how to set up a new business

B ▶ Listen and read.

STARTING A NEW BUSINESS

Many immigrants in the U.S. dream about starting their own business. In 2015, more than 16% of businesses in the U.S. were owned by immigrants. However, there are a lot of **obstacles**.

You might have a great idea, but you also need a strong business plan to succeed. In your business plan, describe your product or service. Explain who your customers are. Include a sales and marketing plan. Finally, think about
5 the different business costs. Here are some tips when starting a new business.

YOUR PRODUCT OR SERVICE
Your business can solve a customer need or problem. First, think about why customers want your product or service. What needs does it meet? Why is it special? How is it better than other products or services?

YOUR MARKET
10 Think about your customers. Are they children, teenagers, or adults? Are they mostly male or female? Where do they live? This information will help you understand your customers.

SALES AND MARKETING PLAN
The sales and **marketing** plan explains how you will communicate with your customers. For example, will you send emails, use online
15 ads, or send **brochure**s? Include information about the price of the product or service. Also describe any special offers. Then think about how you will sell your product or service. Will your business be online only? Do you also need a physical shop?

BUSINESS COSTS
20 Setting up a new business can be expensive. Before you start, try to predict your future costs. Typical costs include rent and insurance. Also, save as much money as possible. Try to predict how much money you will make. Finally, find out what federal or state agencies are available to help you. They may provide financial aid to cover some business costs.

C IDENTIFY. What is the main idea of the article? Circle the correct answer.

   a. Create a strong business plan before starting a new business.
   b. Decide on the best way to communicate with your customers.
   c. Describe how your product is better than other similar products.

D CITE EVIDENCE. Complete the sentences. Where is the information? Write the line number.

Lines

1. In 2015, more than 16% of U.S. businesses _____.
   a. were owned by immigrants
   b. failed in the first year
   c. were online only _____

2. A business plan should describe how a product _____.
   a. will meet customers' needs
   b. is similar to other products
   c. will be delivered to customers _____

3. In your sales plan, you should include information about _____.
   a. business costs
   b. your obstacles
   c. product prices _____

4. Federal or state agencies can help you _____.
   a. find new customers
   b. create online ads
   c. pay some of your expenses _____

E INTERPRET VOCABULARY. Answer the questions.

1. The word *obstacles* in line 2 means _____.
   a. problems
   b. advantages

2. The word *brochure* in line 15 means _____.
   a. an information sheet
   b. a website

3. The word *marketing* in line 13 means _____.
   a. a method to discover and reach new customers
   b. a method to get federal or state supports

F SUMMARIZE. What are the most important ideas in the article? Write three sentences.

_____

_____

_____

Lessons 5 & 6: Grammar

A Cross out the incorrect words.

1. A: How's work?

 B: Terrible! I **am / is** going to look for a new job.

2. A: Where is Jeffrey going to work?

 B: He **is / are** going to work at the restaurant next to school.

3. A: When **is / are** the English class going to start?

 B: Next Tuesday.

4. A: **Is / Are** you going to look for a job online?

 B: Yes, I am.

5. A: **Is / Are** Maha and Jackie going to look at the careers section of the company website?

 B: Yes, they are

B Complete the sentences. Use *is*, *isn't*, *are*, or *aren't*.

1. Aziz ___isn't___ going to apply for a new job because he likes the one he has now.
2. Chen and Ani _____ going to volunteer at the food bank because they want to help other people.
3. Maria and Carmen _____ going to look for a job online because they don't have a computer.
4. Ying Ying _____ going to check the college course catalog to see if she can register next week.
5. Bilan _____ going to go to the meeting because she has a class at the same time.
6. Ahmed and Sarah _____ going to the temp agency because they want to look for office assistant jobs.

C Complete the paragraph. Use a form of *going to* and the verb in parentheses. Use contractions when possible.

Terence and I _____ the job fair tomorrow at school. There will be a
(visit)

lot of companies there. We want to get a job after we graduate.

Terence _____ about office jobs. I _____ about a
(ask)   (find out)

job for project managers. We _____ our hardest to get new jobs soon.
(try)

D Read the text. Correct five more mistakes with *going to.*

Adam works in a factory. He works at night and takes English classes in the

                                                is
morning. He wants a new job. He going to talk to a job counselor at his adult
                                            ∧
school. He is also go to the library to read about different types of jobs. He

wants to start his own business. Adam likes fixing cars, so in the future he

are going to open an auto repair shop. But for now, he wants to get more

experience as a mechanic. So, he is going apply for a job at an auto repair

shop near his home. Adam's wife is also go to look for a job. She wants to

open a childcare business in their home. But first she is going to getting a job

at a daycare center.

E WRITE ABOUT IT. Your goal is to get a better job. Write about three things you're going to do to achieve your goals and two things you're not going to do. Write complete sentences.

I'm not going to quit my job until I find a better job.

_____

_____

_____

_____

_____

Lesson 7: Workplace, Life, and Community Skills

A Complete the chart. Write about things you want to *be*, *do*, and *have*.

Be	Do	Have

B Choose one goal from Exercise A. Write steps to achieve the goal.

Goal: _____

Step 1:

_____

_____

_____

Step 2:

_____

_____

_____

Step 3:

_____

_____

_____

C Look at the results of a survey. Answer the questions.

Obstacles to Student Success in College

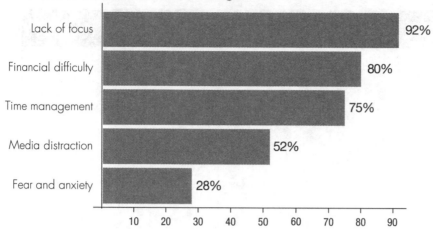

1. What is the biggest obstacle for college students?

_____

2. What is the problem for 52 percent of the students?

_____

3. What is the smallest obstacle for most students?

_____

4. What percent of students have problems managing their time?

_____

5. If 200 people answered this survey, how many students were spending too much time on media, such as TV and their phones?

_____

D WRITE ABOUT IT. Think about a certificate, license, or degree you would like to get. Research it online. Write about any obstacles that may stop you from getting it, and the support available to you.

Obstacles	Support
• too expensive	• offers financial aid

Lesson 8: Writing

A Read the Writing Skill. Then put the steps in order.

Writing Skill: Write supporting sentences
Remember that the topic sentence gives the main idea of the paragraph. Supporting sentences give more information to support the topic sentence. When supporting sentences are steps, they begin with words such as *first*, *second*, *then*, *next*, *last*, or *finally*.

____ Next, I will pass the automotive service exam and receive my certificate.

_1_ First, I'm going to work and study English.

____ Then, I will work part-time and study full-time for one year.

____ Finally, I will look for full-time work.

____ Second, I will apply for a community college program in automobile servicing.

B Circle the topic sentence for the paragraph in Exercise A.

a. My goal is to work and learn English.
b. My goal is to become an auto body repairer.
c. My goal is to study in a community college.

C Read the text. Correct five more mistakes.

My goal is to ~~became~~ *become* a welder. First, I need to improve my English. This fall, I am going enroll in a six-month language course. Then, I will apply at a welding training program at a community college. Next, I will pass the test and start looking for work at a manufacturing company. I might worked under a licensed welder for two years to get experience. Final, I will work for myself. My friend also works as a welder. I'll to meet him tomorrow to talk about how to start my own business.

Lesson 9 & 10: Grammar

A Complete the sentences. Use the present continuous for the future.

1. I _____ *am helping* _____ with the beach trash clean-up this weekend.
(help)

2. My husband _____ this weekend because he has to work.
(not / volunteer)

3. Alice and Dan _____ at home tonight because they are going to help with
(not / stay)

the food drive.

4. Sam _____ a mural on the wall at the park this weekend.
(paint)

5. My sister and I _____ to organize the party on Sunday.
(help)

B Write questions. Use the present continuous for the future.

1. (help / when / at the community center / he)

_____

2. (classes for adults / the community center / offer)

_____

3. (do / she / what / tomorrow night)

_____

4. (soon / get / you / your degree)

_____

C WRITE ABOUT IT. What are your plans for the weekend? Write three sentences using the present continuous.

This weekend, I'm volunteering at the community center.

_____

_____

_____

Lesson 11: Soft Skills at Work

A UNDERSTAND. Complete the sentence.

A person who takes responsibility for his or her professional growth is someone who tries to _____.

    a. have a good work/life balance

    b. learn new skills

    c. get along with co-workers

B IDENTIFY. Read the paragraphs. In which situations do the people take responsibility for their professional growth? Check (✓) the situations.

❑ **1.** Eden works as a receptionist at a hotel. However, her goal is to become a computer programmer and work in a software company. Two nights a week, she takes a computer programming course at her local community college.

❑ **2.** Lukas is a food preparation worker. His goal is to start his own bakery. However, he thinks there will be a lot of obstacles in his way. He decides to stay in the same position, and he hopes that he will get a promotion in the future.

❑ **3.** Ahmet is an accountant, but he wants to become an accountant manager. First, he signs up for an online management course. Then, he passes the course exam. After that, he asks his manager for more responsibilities where he can use his new skills. Finally, he gets a promotion in his company.

❑ **4.** Rose is a dental assistant. She would like to take a course to become a licensed dental hygienist, but the tuition is very expensive. She decides to apply for financial aid. Then, she gets enough money to take the course. She works hard and passes the final exam.

C ANALYZE. Read the situations in Exercise B again. What are the different ways the people take responsibility for their professional growth?

❑   **a.** take classes to get a better job

❑   **b.** find out what help is available

❑   **c.** wait to see if they will get a promotion

❑   **d.** practice new skills

❑   **e.** take action to achieve goals

Unit 3: Going to School

Lesson 1: Vocabulary

A Complete the sentences. Use the words in the box.

figure out	go online	look up a word	make up a test

1. Joan always asks her teacher if she can't _____ an answer.

2. Lucy likes to _____ when she doesn't understand something she's reading.

3. Lamisa likes to _____ and surf the internet.

4. Tim was out sick. Luckily, Mr. Regan allowed him to _____ that he missed.

B Match the expressions with the definitions. Write the correct letter.

1. do research _____   **a.** review homework with the teacher

2. go online _____   **b.** look for information about a topic

3. go over homework _____   **c.** give the teacher a completed assignment

4. hand in homework _____   **d.** use the internet

C Complete the sentences. Use the activities in the box.

do research	go over homework	go online
hand in homework	make up a test	~~go to a parent-teacher conference~~

1. Dora is going to _go to a parent-teacher conference_ with Ms. Tanner and talk about her daughter's grades.

2. If you _____ late, the teacher will take off points.

3. For his school project, Danny first decided to _____.
   But he could not find all the information he needed, so he decided to also
   _____ at the library.

4. The teacher takes time every morning to _____ from the last class.

5. Carl needs to do his homework and _____ if he wants to pass his science class.

D WRITE ABOUT IT. Write about study activities you would like to do in your English class. Underline the activities you choose.

I would like to <u>do research</u> on American history. I would like to <u>go online</u> at the school library to do this research. I will <u>look up words</u> I don't know in my dictionary.

_____

_____

_____

Lessons 2 & 3: Grammar

A Read the list. Complete the sentences. Cross out the incorrect words.

> • Math homework is due every Friday—no exceptions!
> • You must bring a notebook and a dictionary to every class.
> • We recommend that all ESL students take ESL Reading.
> • It is a good idea to visit the tutoring center for help after school.
> • The English test is going to be next Wednesday. You can't make up the test!

1. Students **have to / should** hand in math homework every Friday.

2. Students **have to / should** bring a notebook and a dictionary to every class.

3. ESL students **have to / should** take ESL Reading.

4. Students **have to / should** go to the tutoring center after school.

B Complete the conversations. Use the correct form of the verbs.

1. **A:** _____ my son _____ computer science to graduate from
           (do)   (have to / take)

   high school?

   B: No, he _____ .
           (do / not)

2. **A:** How can we find out about financial aid?

   B: You _____ to a counselor.
          (should / talk)

3. **A:** How can my children improve their grades?

   B: They _____ every day after school.
           (should / study)

4. **A:** _____ I _____ English with my son's teacher?
           (do)   (have to / speak)

   B: No, you _____. There is a translator if you need one.
           (do / not)

C Write questions for the answers.

1. **Q:** _____.

   A: Yes, you should. You should take the English placement test.

2. **Q:** _____.

   A: Yes, he does. The last day to register is September 15.

Lesson 4: Reading

A DEVELOP YOUR ACADEMIC SKILLS. Read the Academic Skill. What do you already know about study tips? Complete the sentence.

Time management is _____.
- **a.** a subject that should be taught in school
- **b.** a way of making the most of your time
- **c.** a skill used by students taking business classes

B ▶ Listen and read.

TOP TIPS FOR TIME MANAGEMENT

All students have to know how to use their time well. Good time management can help you achieve great results.

GET ORGANIZED

5 The first step is to organize your time. Do one task at a time, so your studying does not become **overwhelming**. You should study a little every day and avoid cramming before a test. This way you will be rested and ready to do well.

10 Another good tip is to do work gradually, well in advance of tests or deadlines. You should allow plenty of time to get work done. Doing a little bit of work at a time means you can focus better. Your work will be better as a result. It also

15 reduces stress because you know you have a plan for your work.

Ben's timetable   Feb 3 - Feb 7, 2020

DAY	4:30-5:00	5:00-5:15	5:15-5:45	5:45-6:45	6:45-7:45
MONDAY	Math homework	Break	English homework	Dinner / Soccer	Study for music test
TUESDAY	U.S. history homework	Break	Plan art project	Dinner / Guitar	Read new chemistry lesson again
WEDNESDAY	English homework	Break	Study French verbs	Dinner / TV	Music homework
THURSDAY	Chemistry homework	Break	Geography homework	Dinner / Jog	Study for math test
FRIDAY	French homework	Break	Read about George Washington	Dinner	Night off! Get ready for beach tomorrow

MAKE A REALISTIC SCHEDULE

Create a realistic study timetable for yourself. Keep it simple and carefully plan it. It should include time for homework, study, and activities. A detailed timetable will help you feel in control of your studies. It is easy to
20 focus on subjects you like, but don't neglect other subjects. You need to work on everything.

A timetable should also include regular breaks. Make sure to take time off on the weekend. When you know you have studied well, it is easier to relax with family and friends.

USE DIGITAL TOOLS

There are lots of useful tools you can use to make studying easier. It is easy to create an online calendar with your
25 study, tests, and **assignments**. Then, you can set alarms on your phone to get work done early in the morning. You can also use your phone's timer to mark the end of each study period.

There are also many online resources to help keep track of your time. Some apps show all your school work, grades, and activities. This makes it easy to see what your week looks like and how you are progressing. Other apps prevent you from using websites and apps that waste time. This helps you to focus and complete work more
30 quickly.

C IDENTIFY. What is the main idea of the article? Circle the correct answer.

It is important to _____.
   a. use time well and stick to study plans
   b. allow extra time to study before tests
   c. avoid studying online and on weekends

D CITE EVIDENCE. Complete the sentences. Where is the information? Write the line number.

Lines

1. It is best to _____ so that you do not feel stressed.
   a. concentrate on one subject at a time   **b.** study a lot before a test
   c. focus on weaker subjects

_____

2. A schedule makes time off enjoyable because _____.
   a. your family will be more relaxed   **b.** you know you have worked hard
   c. you can talk to friends about studying

_____

3. Using online apps and technology _____ to develop good study habits.
   a. can be a useful way   **b.** is the only way   **c.** is not the right way

_____

E INTERPRET. Complete the sentences about Ben's timetable.

1. How much time does Ben usually spend on homework and study each night?
   a. 30 minutes   **b.** 60 minutes   **c.** 120 minutes

2. How can Ben see quickly what he has to do that day?
   a. Homework, study, and free time are at the same times every day.
   b. Homework, study, and free time are on separate timetables.
   c. Homework, study, and free time are in different colors.

3. What time does Ben finish studying on Friday?
   a. 5:45   **b.** 6:45   **c.** 7:45

F INTERPRET VOCABULARY. Complete the sentences about the study timetable.

1. The word *overwhelming* in line 7 means _____.
   a. very complicated   **b.** too much to deal with

2. The word *assignments* in line 25 means _____.
   a. a piece of work you have to do   **b.** an after-school activity

G SUMMARIZE. What are the most important ideas in the article? Write three sentences.

_____

_____

_____

Lessons 5: Writing

A Read the Writing Skill. Underline three reasons.

Languages in schools
Many students think math and science are more useful subjects than languages. I don't believe this to be true. First, speaking a second language helps you connect with more people. Second, learning another language makes you stand out from other workers. Finally, knowing more than one language is important for some government jobs.

> **Writing Skill: Support an opinion with reasons**
> Writers sometimes give an opinion about a topic and try to persuade the reader to agree. To persuade or convince the reader, the opinion must be supported with reasons. The words *first*, *second*, and *finally* help organize these reasons.

B Put the sentences in the correct order. Write the numbers on the lines.

___ Second, it makes students learn about teamwork.

___ It is important for all students to take a P.E. class.

___ First, it helps students stay fit and healthy.

___ Finally, it is a great way to reduce stress.

C Read the text. Correct five more mistakes.

Martin ~~want~~ *wants* to go to a community college when he graduates from high school. His school counselor says he has to take three year of English and social studies. He needs to study two years of math, science and P.E. He has take one year of spanish. He should also choose electives in subjects, like life skills and music. He should think carefully about what course he would like to take in college. He has to worry about choosing a major now. He has his school counselor to help him.

Lesson 6 & 7: Grammar

A Put the words in the correct order.

1. (important / very / it's / on time / to hand in homework)

_____

2. (a good idea / punctual / to be / all the time / it's)

_____

3. (information / it's / sometimes / difficult / new / to remember)

_____

4. (necessary / often / to study / before a test / hard / it's)

_____

B Write sentences with *It's* + adjective (or noun phrase) + infinitive.

1. **A:** I'm always tired in class.

   B: _____It's important to sleep_____ for eight hours every night.
   (important / sleep)

2. **A:** I always get to school late!

   B: _____ your home 20 minutes earlier.
   (a good idea / leave)

3. **A:** I have a parent-teacher conference tomorrow.

   B: _____ a little early for the parent-teacher conference.
   (a good idea / you / arrive)

4. **A:** I couldn't understand my French teacher in class yesterday.

   B: _____ her to speak more slowly or to repeat.
   (difficult / ask)

C WRITE ABOUT IT. Your daughter is starting high school. Give her advice on how to do well.

It's a good idea to write down your schedule. It's important to show up on time for class.

_____

_____

_____

Lesson 8: Workplace, Life, and Community Skills

A Look at Lucy's fall report card. Read each statement below. Circle *True* or *False*.

Bay View High School Report Card

Student: Lucy Campos   **Grade:** 10   **Year:** 2019 - 2020

Class	Teacher	Q1	Q2	Q3	Q4	Final	Comments
Art	Smith	A					Follows all directions.
English 2	Fraser	B+					Good student, but needs to pay more attention in class.
Algebra 2	Sherman	C+					Does not complete all homework.
Phys. Ed.	Botros	A–					Participates well.
Chemistry	Suzuki	C					Needs to improve performance on tests. Please call me.
U.S. History	Carroll	A–					Great job on research paper and quizzes.
Spanish 2	Salas	A–					Missing two quizzes.

1. Lucy got good grades in Art, Physical Education, and Algebra 2.   True   False
2. Lucy's highest grade is in Spanish 2.   True   False
3. Lucy needs to work harder in Chemistry and Algebra 2.   True   False
4. Lucy is missing two Spanish 2 homework assignments.   True   False
5. The last name of Lucy's math teacher is Sherman.   True   False
6. This report card is for the fourth quarter of the school year.   True   False

B May is having trouble in school. Read the transcript of a voicemail from May's teacher. Complete the sentences.

1:47 PM	**Voicemail**	100%

Hi, Mr. Lin, This is Ms. Novak, May's math teacher. Your daughter is struggling in my class. May was a great student last quarter. She answered questions in class, studied hard, and got an A on her Algebra test. Now, she is doing poorly in class, and her Algebra test scores were low last week. She did not hand in her homework on time this week.

Please call me. I'd like to help. My number is (925) 555-1546.

▌▌ 0:05 ━━━━━━━━━━━━━━━━━━━━━━━━━━━━━━━━━━━ -0:54

1. Ms. Novak calls Mr. Lin because _____.
   a. his daughter is doing well in class
   b. his daughter got an A on a test
   c. she wants to help his daughter improve right away

2. May did well on her test _____.
   a. last week
   b. this week
   c. last quarter

3. May did not _____ this week.
   a. take the Algebra test
   b. hand in her homework
   c. come to class

4. Mr. Lin needs to _____.
   a. tell May Ms. Novak called
   b. call Ms. Novak back
   c. meet with Ms. Novak

C WRITE ABOUT IT. Imagine you're Mr. Lin. Write a note to Ms. Novak about May's performance. Give two reasons for May's poor performance and one way that you will help her.

Dear Ms. Novak,

_____

_____

_____

Lesson 9 & 10: Grammar

A Complete the paragraph. Use the simple past of the verbs.

Last year my daughter, Claire, _____ in the fourth grade. One day she
                 1. (be)

_____ home and _____ me that she _____ very upset.
  2. (come)   **3. (tell)**   **4. (be)**

Some students in her class _____ with her during soccer. The girls
                 5. (not / play)

_____ the ball to her. Claire's classmate, Ann, _____ the other girls
  6. (not / pass)   **7. (tell)**

not to pass the ball to Claire. Ann thought it was funny. I _____ to the coach that
                 8. (talk)

night. He said he would talk to Ann. He _____, and since then, Ann and Claire
                 9. (do)

have become good friends.

B Complete the conversation. Use the simple past form of the words in the box.

call	do	happen	not/do	tell

Mrs. Lee: What **(1.)** _____? Why are you crying?

Claire: Ann **(2.)** _____ the girls not to pass the ball to me.

Mrs. Lee: **(3.)** _____ you tell anyone?

Claire: No, I **(4.)** _____.

Mrs. Lee: Your coach **(5.)** _____ today. I will call him again.

C Rewrite the sentences. Use the simple past.

1. Alex hits Yonas in the playground.

_____

2. Gerda writes a mean note about another girl.

_____

3. Susan steals Tom's pencil.

_____

4. Ricardo says mean things about Kelly.

_____

D Match the questions and answers. Write the letter.

1. What happened? _b_   **a.** Yes, I did.
2. Did you tell anyone? ___   ~~**b.**~~ Someone beat me up.
3. Who beat you up? ___   **c.** In the cafeteria.
4. When did this happen? ___   **d.** Jenny.
5. Where did it happen? ___   **e.** On Monday.
6. Who did you tell? ___   **f.** He suspended her.
7. What did he do? ___   **g.** Mr. Franklin.

E Correct five more errors with verbs in the simple past.

                                    got
Yesterday Mrs. Leka ~~get~~ a phone call from the principal. He says that a boy
in Vasil's class threatened him. The boy, Bill, calling Vasil names. Bill also
want to fight Vasil after school. Fortunately, Vasil told his teacher. And the
teacher telling the principal. Bill is suspended for one day.

F WRITE ABOUT IT. Write about a time when you or your child had a problem at school. Answer the questions.

1. What happened?

_____

2. When did it happen?

_____

3. Where did it happen?

_____

4. Did you tell anyone? If yes, who did you tell?

_____

Lesson 11: Soft Skills at Work

A UNDERSTAND. Complete the sentence. Circle the correct answer.

A person who is good at separating work life and home life _____.
   a. wears different clothes at home and at work
   b. does not invite co-workers for dinner
   c. focuses on work during working hours, and on family during time off

B IDENTIFY. Read the conversations at work. In which conversations do the people separate work life and family life? Check (✓) the conversations.

❏ **1. Co-worker:** Are you okay, Kyla? You look worried.

   Kyla: I read an email from my daughter's teacher during my lunch break. He wants to meet with me.

   Co-worker: Is your daughter having trouble at school?

   Kyla: I'm not sure. I'm going to reply to the email after my shift. I'll ask him then.

❏ **2. Worker:** My son's kindergarten just called. It's closing for a snow day. I will have to bring him to work with me.

   Supervisor: No, that's not a good idea. This isn't a safe place for a small child.

   Worker: I guess you're right. I'll ask my neighbor to watch him.

❏ **3. Teacher:** Hello, Ms. Vega. I'd like to talk to you about Teresa's Spanish test. Can you come in one evening this week?

   Ms. Vega: I'm working nights this week, but her father is free on Thursday. He can meet with you then.

   Teacher: That's great. I'll see him on Thursday night.

C ANALYZE. Read the conversations in Exercise B again. What are the different ways the people separate work life and home life?

❏   a. arrange childcare when a child is sick

❏   b. don't take personal calls at work

❏   c. ask someone else to help with family tasks

❏   d. don't read personal emails at work

❏   e. take a few quiet minutes before starting work

Unit 4: Getting a Job

Lesson 1: Vocabulary

A Complete the sentences.

efficient	~~motivated~~	organized	punctual

1. Omar is very ___*motivated*___ to get a promotion. He works very hard.

2. Bill always arrives five minutes early. He's very _____.

3. John doesn't waste time. He's really _____.

4. Alisa keeps her desk in order. She's very _____.

B Match the expressions with the definitions. Write the correct letter.

1. pleasant	___	**a.** helps others
2. hardworking	___	**b.** willing to change
3. cooperative	___	**c.** polite, friendly, or kind
4. dependable	___	**d.** completes a lot of tasks
5. flexible	___	**e.** able to be trusted

C Cross out the incorrect words.

Frank works at an auto repair service center. He is very **punctual / organized** and always arrives at work at 7:55 A.M. He likes working on a team and is very **cooperative / motivated** with his co-workers. Frank also always keeps his work area clean and **organized / efficient**. Frank's customers say he is **punctual / pleasant**.

D Read the job ads. Complete the sentences.

cooperative	dependable	organized	pleasant

1. **Restaurant Hostess Wanted**
   New restaurant in downtown Los Angeles needs a friendly hostess with a _____ attitude. Must be good with the public.

2. **Medical Assistant Needed**
   Busy health clinic needs assistant who can keep track of patient files and make appointments. Must be _____.

3. **Now Hiring Construction Workers**
   Local construction company seeks reliable workers. Must follow instructions and work well in groups. Must be _____.

4. **Home Care Aide**
   Responsibilities: Shop for food, cook, plan meals, do laundry. Provide other assistance to elderly people in their homes. Must be caring and _____.

E WRITE ABOUT IT. What are your best qualities? Complete the sentences.

cooperative	efficient	motivated	pleasant	flexible
hardworking	punctual	organized	dependable	

I am motivated. I always set goals for myself.

1. I am _____. _____.

2. I am _____. _____.

3. I am _____. _____.

Lessons 2 & 3: Grammar

A Complete the sentences. Use past participle form of the verbs in parentheses. Then answer the questions about yourself.

1. **A:** Have you ever ___driven___ a bus?
   (drive)

   B: _No, I haven't._

2. **A:** Have you ever _____ with children?
   (work)

   B: _____

3. **A:** Have you ever _____ in a restaurant?
   (cook)

   B: _____

4. **A:** Have you ever _____ landscaping work?
   (do)

   B: _____

5. **A:** Have you ever _____ a patient's blood pressure?
   (take)

   B: _____

B Complete the conversations. Use the present perfect with *ever* to make questions. Then write short answers.

1. **A:** _____
   (in your community / you / volunteer)

   B: Yes, I _____.

2. **A:** _____
   (customers / she / serve / in a restaurant)

   B: No, she _____.

3. **A:** _____
   (for work / use / they / email)

   B: Yes, they _____.

4. **A:** _____
   (work / he / for a large company)

   B: No, he _____.

Lesson 4: Workplace, Life, and Community Skills

A Carlos Mendoza is applying for a job. Read his job application form. Circle his job duties.

Employment History

Employer (1)	Starting Position	Ending Position	Dates Employed
Angelino's Italian	Cleaner	Server	8/2017 – Present

Work Phone	Pay Rate		Supervisor
(714) 555-4130	$9.75/hr + tips		Pablo Sanchez

Job Duties	Reason for Leaving	
Helped open and close restaurant on Sundays, set up, served customers	Restaurant is closing.	

Address	City	State	Zip
260 W. Topeka Drive	Garden Grove	CA	92840

May we contact this employer?

● Yes ○ No

B Read the statements. Write *T* (true) or *F* (false). Rewrite the false statements to make them true.

1. Carlos's last employer was Angelino's Italian. _____

_____

2. Carlos's supervisor was Pablo Sanchez. _____

_____

3. Carlos started as a server. _____

_____

4. Carlos started working in June 2017. _____

_____

5. Carlos left because he wanted more hours. _____

_____

6. Carlos does not want employers to call Pablo Sanchez for a reference. _____

_____

C WRITE ABOUT IT. Imagine you are completing an online application for a job that you are interested in. Complete it with information about your previous jobs.

Application For Employment

Personal Information

Name	Address	City	State	ZIP

Phone Number	Mobile Number	Email Address

Are you a U.S. citizen? ◯ Yes ◯ No   Have you ever been fired from a job? ◯ Yes   ◯ No

Can you legally work in the U.S.? (If hired, verification within 3 days is required.) ◯ Yes   ◯ No

Position

Position	Available Start Date	Desired Pay

Employment desired ◯ Full-time   ◯ Part-time   ◯ Seasonal/Temporary

Education

School Name	Location	Years Attended	Degree Received

Employment History

Employer (1)	Starting Position	Ending Position	Dates Employed

Job Duties	Reason for Leaving	Supervisor

Employer (2)	Starting Position	Ending Position	Dates Employed

Job Duties	Reason for Leaving	Supervisor

Lessons 5 & 6: Grammar

A It is now the year 2020. Look at the timeline. Read the statements. Write *T* (true) or *F* (false).

2010
Marcus moved to Anaheim, California.

2012
Marcus got a job at Bill's Auto Shop.

2013
Marcus married Maria.

2015
Marcus received ASE Certification.

1. Marcus has lived in Anaheim since 2010.   _____

2. Marcus has been married for six years.   _____

3. Marcus has worked at Bill's Auto Shop since 2012.   _____

4. Marcus has had ASE Certification for five years.   _____

B Cross out the incorrect words.

1. Cassie has been a teacher **for / since** three years.

2. Ardita and Teri have worked here **for / since** last June.

3. Artur's employer has been on vacation **for / since** two weeks.

4. Sasha has worked as an architect **for / since** five years.

C Write the present perfect form of the verbs in parentheses.

1. Alice _____ at City Hospital for three years.
     (volunteer)

2. Bill _____ his own lawn service since 2008.
     (have)

3. Jun _____ an HVAC mechanic since 2003.
     (be)

4. We _____ customers here for eight years.
     (serve)

D Write statements about Ali's résumé. Use *for* or *since*.

Ali Kateb
110 W. Olive Avenue
Duarte, CA 91016
(626) 888-8000

Work Experience

| 2017 – present | Assistant Manager |
| | Big Olly's Tires, Duarte, CA |

| 2014 – 2017 | Lead Technician/Installer |
| | Big Olly's Tires, Duarte, CA |

Training

| 2014 | ASE Certificate |

Volunteer Experience

| 2014 – present | Auto Shop Mechanic, Valley Teen Ranch |
| | Teaching teenagers how to repair cars |

1. *He has worked at Big Olly's Tires since 2014.*

2. _____

3. _____

4. _____

E WRITE ABOUT IT. Have you worked since you came to the United States? What job(s) have you held? For how long or since when?

I have worked in a restaurant since I came to the United States.

I came here in 2015. I have been a line cook since 2016.

In 2017, I got a second job at a grocery store. I have worked there for two years.

_____

_____

_____

Lesson 7: Reading

 A ▶ Listen and read.

SIX TIPS FOR A SUCCESSFUL INTERVIEW

Interviews can be stressful. However, with the right preparation, you can succeed and get that job!

DO YOUR HOMEWORK!
It's important to have the right skills and qualifications. However, you also need to understand the job. Before the interview, read the description carefully. Look at the responsibilities. Think about how your skills match them.
5 You should also check out the company's social media pages. During the interview, talk about any **recent** achievements the company had. This shows you're interested in the company.

Also, know your résumé well! Think about your experience. Give examples of when you achieved something. How did you solve a problem? What examples show that you are dependable and hardworking?

KNOW THE TYPE OF INTERVIEW
10 Most interviews are face-to-face. However, many interviews are now done online. For video interviews, make sure your **webcam** is working. Also choose a room that is quiet and bright.

PRACTICE, PRACTICE, PRACTICE
Practice some common interview questions. These include:

* Tell me about yourself.
15 * What's your biggest weakness?
* Why did you apply for this role?
* What do you know about the company?

BE PUNCTUAL
To make a good impression, arrive 10 minutes early. Check bus and train
20 routes, and find the quickest way to get to the company's office. If your interview is in the morning, traffic may also be a problem.

LOOK PROFESSIONAL
The way you dress says a lot about you. To look professional, wear a dark-colored suit and shoes – never sneakers! Don't use too much perfume. Women should avoid wearing too much jewelry or makeup. Make sure
25 your clothes are clean. And check that your hair is neat, even for **casual** interviews.

BE CONFIDENT
It's OK to feel **nervous** before an interview. However, try to stay calm. Make eye contact with the interviewer. Stand and sit up straight. Finally, remember to smile!

To succeed in your interview, follow these tips. And remember -- prepare, prepare again, and finally, prepare!

 B DEVELOP YOUR ACADEMIC SKILLS. Read the Academic Skill. Answer the question.

The writer says, "Do your homework!" You can infer that you should _____.

   a. start a new course
   b. find out about a company
   c. clean your house

> **Academic Skill:**
> **Make Inferences**
>
> In an article, some ideas are not stated directly. Readers must guess or infer these ideas as they read.

C IDENTIFY. What is the main idea of the article? Circle the correct answer.

    a. Get a professional service to help you write your résumé.

    b. You should always take the train to an interview.

    c. Do lots of preparation before going for your interview.

D CITE EVIDENCE. Complete the sentences. Where is the information? Write the line number.

Lines

1. You should think about how to match _____ to the job responsibilities before the interview.

    a. your skills   **b.** your clothes   **c.** the type of interview   _____

2. Know your work history well so that you can _____.

    a. talk about your social media pages   **b.** show how you solved problems   _____

    c. prepare for a video interview

3. For video interviews, make sure that _____.

    a. you arrive 10 minutes early   **b.** there are no mistakes in your résumé _____

    c. your webcam is working

4. If your interview is in the morning, remember that _____.

    a. traffic may cause a delay   **b.** you might be tired   _____

    c. you should look professional

E INTERPRET VOCABULARY. Answer the questions.

1. The word *webcam* in line 11 means _____.

    a. a camera connected to the internet   **b.** a video application

2. The word *recent* in line 5 means _____.

    a. in the near past   **b.** in the near future

3. The word *casual* in line 25 means _____.

    a. formal   **b.** informal

4. The word *nervous* in line 27 means _____.

    a. talkative   **b.** worried

F SUMMARIZE. What are the most important ideas in the article? Write three sentences

_____

_____

_____

Lesson 8: Writing

A Read the Writing Skill. Match the questions with the details.

1. Dear Mr. Mahad, ___c___

2. I got my degree in nursing in 2012. _____

3. I have six years of experience. _____

4. I would like to apply for the position of nurse. _____

5. I was a nurse in China before moving to the U.S. _____

a. What job are you applying for?

b. Where did you work before?

c. Who are you writing to?

d. Why do you think you are qualified?

e. When did you graduate?

B Which question from Exercise A is answered in the following paragraph? Circle the correct letter.

I have a state license, and I have worked as a dental assistant for three years. I have never missed a day at work. I am very dependable, hardworking, and pleasant to work with.

    a.   **b.**   **c.**   **d.**   **e.**

C Read the cover letter. Correct four more errors.

Dear Mr. Popov,

I am writing to ~~applies~~ *apply* for the position of electrician at Energy Electric Co. I am qualified for this position because I am a licensed electrician and have experience in this area. I worked for an electrical services company in turkey since two years before I moved to the U.S. in 2015. Since then, I have work under a licensed electrician and have received a certificate in electrical engineering. Finally, I am hard working and dependable, and I am motivated to do well in this job.

Thank you for your time and consideration. I look forward to hearing from you.

Sincerely,

Ahmed Jibril

Lessons 9 & 10: Grammar

A Put the words in the correct order.

1. (soccer / play / I / used to)

   I used to play soccer.

2. (dancing / Olga / go / used to)

   _____

3. (in Mexico / Mr. and Mrs. Garcia / used to / live)

   _____

4. (play / he / used to / chess)

   _____

5. (used to / Ting / the guitar / play)

   _____

B Complete the paragraph. Use *used to* and the verbs in the box.

have	listen	play	swim	walk	~~do~~

Hector is from El Salvador. Now he lives in Austin, Texas. He likes his new home, but he

misses some of the things he ___used to do___. He _____ to the market every morning

to get breakfast. He also _____ his guitar in the park in the evenings. His friends

_____ to him play. He also _____ at the beach a lot. He _____ a

bicycle that he rode to work every day.

C Read the sentences. Correct the errors with *used to* + verb.

1. Royce ~~use~~ *used* to play basketball every Friday.

2. Edwina and Julia used go to the beach on Sundays.

3. Trung used do go to the farmers market in the morning.

4. Marta use eat her biggest meal at lunch.

Lesson 11: Soft Skills at Work

A UNDERSTAND. Complete the sentence.

A person who is positive _____.
- **a.** is very organized
- **b.** complains about work
- **c.** finds something good in bad situations

B IDENTIFY. Read the conversations at work. In which conversations does someone have a positive attitude? Check (✓) the conversations.

❑ **1. Sam:** I have never been so busy! The boss has given me so much work to do! I feel really stressed out.

    Sara: That's too bad, but look at it this way. He probably thinks you're very dependable. He wouldn't give you so much work if he didn't think you could handle it.

❑ **2. Hamza:** I hate getting up early for work. I am always so tired in the morning.

    David: I know, but at least we get to finish early, too. This means we can spend more time with our family and friends in the evening.

    Hamza: Yes, you're right.

❑ **3. Alice:** Hi Adam. Is everything OK? You look angry.

    Adam: Yes, I am. I've been waiting for the meeting room for 15 minutes but the supervisor is still in there! I need to get ready for my presentation.

    Alice: I'm sorry to hear that. But maybe you can use this time to do something else, like reviewing your notes for the presentation.

C ANALYZE. Read the conversations in Exercise B again. What are the different ways the people show they are positive?

❑   **a.** talk about people's positive qualities

❑   **b.** consider the good side of a problem

❑   **c.** complain about other people

❑   **d.** support people in difficult situations

❑   **e.** tell people what qualities they need to improve

Unit 5: Traveling

Lesson 1: Vocabulary

A Label the pictures.

| carry-on bag | ticket agent | arrivals and departures display |
| boarding pass | passenger | X-ray machine |

1. _____

2. _____

3. _____

4. _____

5. _____

6. _____

B Match the words with the definitions. Write the correct letter.

1. luggage _____ a. a small structure or machine where you can buy things

2. luggage tags _____ b. a ticket to fly to a destination

3. metal detector _____ c. identification information

4. kiosk _____ d. an electronic device that gives a signal when it's close to metal

5. e-ticket _____ e. bags and suitcases

C Read the statements. Circle the correct answers.

1. This is the place in the airport where passengers board a plane.

   a. gate   **b.** security   **c.** arrivals and departures display

2. Passengers must walk through this before they board a plane.

   a. kiosk   **b.** metal detector   **c.** X-ray machine

3. Carry-on bags must pass through this.

   a. metal detector   **b.** X-ray machine   **c.** kiosk

4. Passengers can get flight information from this person.

   a. ticket agent   **b.** security agent   **c.** pilot

5. Passengers can buy tickets from this machine.

   a. metal detector   **b.** gate   **c.** kiosk

D Is it a person, place, or thing? Complete the chart.

metal detector	luggage	e-ticket	kiosk
gate	passenger	~~ticket agent~~	security agent

Person	Place	Thing
ticket agent		

E WRITE ABOUT IT. Have you ever forgotten anything when you traveled? What happened?

One time, I forgot my carry-on bag in a taxi. I forgot the bag in the trunk. The taxi driver called me the next day. I had a luggage tag on the bag. I picked it up from him and thanked him.

_____

_____

_____

_____

_____

Lessons 2 & 3: Grammar

A Cross out the incorrect words.

1. Last night when we packed our bags, we **can't / couldn't** find our toothpaste.

2. Remember that you **can't / couldn't** bring more than two carry-on bags on the plane.

3. She **can / would** ask the ticket agent to change her seat when we get to the terminal.

4. They **will be / were** able to change their reservation last night.

5. We **can't / couldn't** get to the airport on time because there was too much traffic.

6. They **were / weren't** able to buy a magazine at the store because they didn't have time.

7. Our gate is a long way from here but we **will / won't** be able to get there on time because we're early.

8. He **could / couldn't** find his luggage at baggage claim, so he asked for help.

9. Because of a mechanical problem, our plane **will / won't** be able to take off for another 20 minutes.

10. She **was / wasn't** able to board because she lost her boarding pass.

B Complete the conversation.

can	can't	couldn't	was able to

1. **A:** I had trouble hearing the announcement. Did you hear it?

   B: No, I _____ hear it either.

2. **A:** Excuse me, sir. You _____ bring that water bottle on the plane. You have

   two choices. You _____ drink it now or throw it out.

   B: OK, thanks. I will drink it now.

3. **A:** How was the overnight flight?

   B: It was good. I _____ sleep on the plane and get some rest.

Lesson 4: Workplace, Life, and Community Skills

A Look at the map of the airport terminal. Circle the place where you can check in luggage at the curb.

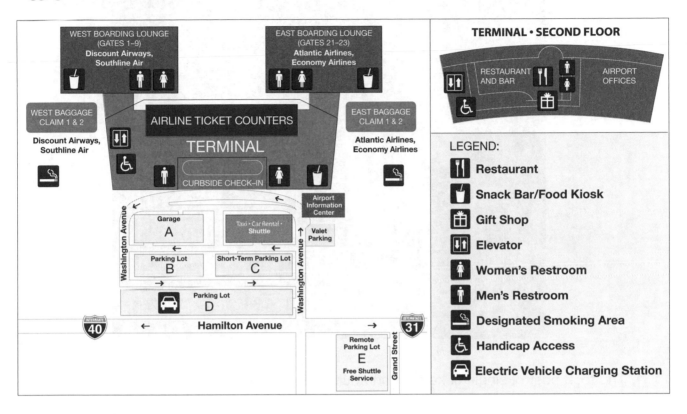

B Look at the map again. Read the questions. Circle the correct answers.

1. Which parking lot is for short-term parking?
   a. B   **b.** C   **c.** D

2. Where is the restaurant?
   a. Terminal – First Floor   **b.** Terminal – Second Floor   **c.** East Boarding Lounge

3. You have a flight on Atlantic Airlines. Which gate could your flight take off from?
   a. Gate 1   **b.** Gate 5   **c.** Gate 21

4. Where can you get a taxi?
   a. Washington Avenue   **b.** Parking Lot   **c.** Grand Street

5. Your flight is on Discount Airways. Which baggage claim should you go to?
   a. West Baggage Claim 1 or 2
   b. East Baggage Claim 2
   c. East Baggage Claim 1 or 2

C Look at the ticket price chart for public transportation. Complete the sentences. Circle the correct answers.

	Zone A	Zone B	Zone C
ADULT			
Single	$2.00	$2.50	$3.00
Return	$3.50	$4.00	$5.00
Weekly pass	$15.00	$18.00	$20.00
Monthly pass	$55.00	$65.00	$75.00
CHILD (9–17) (8 or under-free)			
Single	$1.20	$1.50	$1.75
Return	$2.00	$2.50	$3.00
Weekly pass	$8.00	$10.00	$12.00
Monthly pass	$27.00	$35.00	$42.00

1. The total cost of single tickets for an adult and a 9-year old child to Zone C is _____.
  a. $4.50
  b. $4.75
  c. $5.00

2. $55 is the cost of _____.
  a. an adult monthly pass to Zone B
  b. a child monthly pass to Zone C
  c. an adult monthly pass to Zone A

3. Two single tickets for two 10-year old children to Zone B cost _____.
  a. $3.00
  b. $2.50
  c. $2.40

D Read the statements. Write *T* (true) or *F* (false).

1. The cost of an adult single to Zone A is the same as a child return to Zone A. _____

2. An adult single to Zone C is more expensive than an adult return to Zone A. _____

3. The adult monthly pass to Zone C is the most expensive ticket. _____

4. It's cheaper to buy four return tickets for children that are nine years and older to Zone B than to get one week pass for the same zone. _____

Lessons 5 & 6: Grammar

A Complete the conversations. Use the words in the box.

hers	mine	my	their	your	yours

1. **A:** Who's picking us up at the airport?

   B: My parents. Wait. I think that's _____ car.

2. **A:** Is this her carry-on bag?

   B: No. _____ is in the bin.

3. **A:** Where is _____ backpack?

   B: It's on your back!

4. **A:** Where are my sunglasses?

   B: _____ sunglasses are in your luggage.

5. **A:** Is this _____ ?

   B: Yes, that's mine.

6. **A:** We need to drive to the airport, but I think my car is low on gas.

   B: That's OK. Let's take _____ instead.

B Change the underlined words to possessive pronouns.

1. My suitcase is in the overhead bin. ~~Her suitcase~~ *Hers* is under her seat.

2. He printed his e-ticket last night. I printed <u>my e-ticket</u> this morning.

3. Peter and Maya were worried that their bus was canceled. But luckily, <u>their bus</u> was the last one to leave before the storm got worse.

4. The airline lost his bag but luckily they didn't lose <u>her bag</u>.

5. The flight attendant asked everyone to turn off their cell phones. So my brother turned <u>his cell phone</u> off.

6. Do you have your ticket? I only have <u>my ticket</u>.

C Complete the conversations. Use *is* or *are*.

1. **A:** Is this our luggage?

   B: Ours _is_ in the shuttle.

2. **A:** I can't find our gate.

   B: Ours _____ over there, next to the restaurant.

3. **A:** Are these your books?

   B: No. Mine _____ in my bag.

4. **A:** Is this her rental car?

   B: No. Hers _____ behind that red car.

5. **A:** Is this your seat?

   B: Yes, it _____ mine.

D Complete the conversations. Use possessive adjectives or possessive pronouns.

1. **A:** Is this _his_ travel case?

   B: No. His is in the car.

2. **A:** Is this _____ suitcase?

   B: Yes. That is hers.

3. **A:** Are those our bags?

   B: Yes, they are _____.

4. **A:** Where is _____ boarding pass?

   B: He's not sure. He put it down somewhere in the restaurant.

5. **A:** Excuse me. I went through security, and now I can't find _____ keys.

   B: Are these _____ keys in the bin?

   A: Oh, yes, those are _____.

Lesson 7: Workplace, Life, and Community Skills

A ▶ Listen and read.

IMPORTANT TIPS FOR FLYING ABROAD

Are you traveling outside the U.S. by air soon? Do you know what you need to bring? People sometimes forget important things before they travel
5 abroad. They can then have serious problems. Here are five tips to help you avoid these problems.

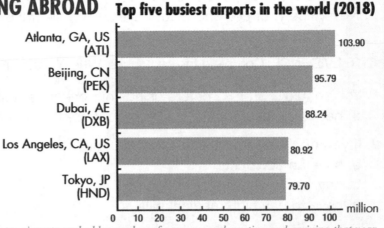

Top five busiest airports in the world (2018)

Note: airports ranked by number of passengers departing and arriving that year.

CONTACT YOUR BANK
Let your bank know when you're
10 traveling abroad. Tell them if you're going to use your credit card there. If your bank doesn't know, they might think someone has stolen your card when you use it abroad. If they cancel it, you won't be able to use it again. Also, ask your bank to give you some
15 local currency. You may be charged a large fee if you take out cash using your card at your **destination**.

CHECK YOUR CELL PHONE PLAN
Most U.S. cell phones can be used aboard. However, these calls and texts may not be included in your plan. Many people often come back after a vacation to find a huge phone bill! Contact your cell phone company. Find out what the different **fees** are for using your phone abroad.

20 ### GET TRAVEL INSURANCE
Unfortunately, accidents can happen. If you don't have insurance, hospital and medical bills can be very expensive. Get the right travel insurance for your needs.

HAVE ALL YOUR TRAVEL DOCUMENTS
Find out if you need a visa to enter the country you are traveling to. This is a special government document that
25 allows you to travel in certain countries. Check your passport's **expiration** date. For some countries, it must be valid for at least six months from your departure date. On the day you travel, also make sure you have your e-ticket and your boarding pass.

CHECK THE AIRLINE LUGGAGE POLICY
Do you know how many carry-on bags you can bring? What is the maximum weight and size allowed for
30 suitcases? This information can help you avoid delays – and extra fees – when checking in.

By following these tips, you can avoid some of the stress of flying abroad.

◀   ▶

B DEVELOP YOUR ACADEMIC SKILLS. Read the Academic Skill. Circle the correct answer.

Look at the context of the word *abroad* in line 5. This word means _____.

a. late at night
b. to a foreign country
c. by road

> **Academic Skill:**
> **Get meaning from context**
>
> You can sometimes guess the meaning of a word from the words or sentences around it.

C IDENTIFY. What is the main idea of the article?

    a. You can avoid problems by preparing for your flight abroad.
    b. There are lots of ways to save money in a foreign country.
    c. Never use your cell phone to make calls while traveling abroad.

D CITE EVIDENCE. Complete the sentences. Where is the information? Write the line number.

Lines

1. You should _____ before using your credit card abroad.
    a. get travel insurance   **b.** tell your bank   **c.** get some local money   _____

2. If you don't get travel insurance, you might _____.
    a. have an accident
    b. have an expensive cell phone bill
    c. have to pay high medical bills   _____

3. A visa is a government document that allows you to _____.
    a. visit some countries
    b. use your cell phone abroad
    c. use your credit card abroad   _____

E INTERPRET. Complete the sentences about the chart.

1. Only one airport has _____ million passengers in 2018.
    a. under 80   **b.** over 80   **c.** over 90

2. The difference between the second and the fifth busiest airports is _____ million passengers.
    a. 15.50   **b.** 16.09   **c.** 17.90

F INTERPRET VOCABULARY.

1. The word *destination* in line 15 means _____.
    a. a place you're going to   **b.** an airline you're using

2. The word *fees* in line 19 means _____.
    a. special offers   **b.** money you pay for a service

3. The words *expiration* date in line 25 mean _____.
    a. the last day something can be used   **b.** the day of your flight

G SUMMARIZE. What are the most important ideas in the article? Write three sentences.

_____

_____

_____

Lesson 8: Writing

A Read the Writing Skill. Then put the steps in order.

___ Second, create an account.

___ Next, go to the bike station and type in your account number to pick up a bike.

_1_ First, find the bike-share company's website or app.

___ After that, use the map to find the nearest bike station to your destination.

___ Finally, cycle to the other bike station and leave your bike there.

___ Then, use the bike-share map to find the nearest bike station to your location.

> **Writing Skill: Use time-order words**
>
> Supporting sentences sometimes describe the steps in a process. Put the steps in order from first to last. Use time-order words and phrases such as *first*, *then*, and *after that*.

B Read the paragraph. Add time-order words to each sentence

This is how to get your airline e-ticket. _____, go to the airline website.

_____, log into your account. _____, click "Manage your flight".

_____, confirm your flight number. _____ click "Get your e-ticket".

C Read the text. Correct four more mistakes.

This is how to use a map app to get to your destination quickly. ~~Then~~, tap on the map app on yours phone. It will show you current location. Next, type in where you want to go, and tap on the directions button. After, the app will show you different ways of getting to our destination, such as by driving, using public transportation, cycling, or walking. Finally, you can't choose the quickest option by comparing the different lengths of time.

(First)

Lessons 9 & 10: Grammar

A Put the words in the correct order. Write questions.

1. (the time / me / could / tell / you)

   _____

2. (a soda / will / me / get / you)

   _____

3. (my bags / help me / you / would / with)

   _____

4. (you / for me / could / the train schedule / check)

   _____

5. (tell / can / me / you / when / will arrive / the bus)

   _____

B Write short answers.

1. **A:** Can I please sit here?

   B: Yes, ___*you can*___.

2. **A:** May I leave my bag here?

   B: Yes, _____.

3. **A:** Can I eat on the train?

   B: No, _____.

4. **A:** Could I change seats with you?

   B: Yes, _____.

5. **A:** May I get off here?

   B: No, _____. Sorry about that.

6. **A:** Could I please change my ticket?

   B: No, I'm sorry, _____.

Lesson 11: Soft Skills at Work

A UNDERSTAND. Complete the sentence.

A person who is good at finding creative solutions _____ to solve problems.
  - **a.** asks a supervisor for help
  - **b.** thinks of new ideas
  - **c.** follows written instructions

B IDENTIFY. Read the situations at work. In which situations do the people find creative solutions to problems? Check (✓) the situations.

❏ **1.** Alex has an important meeting at 9.30 A.M. On his way to work, his car breaks down. Then, he remembers that he has a ride-share app on his phone. He requests a ride, is quickly picked up, and arrives on time for the meeting.

❏ **2.** Hassan owns a small bakery. A customer calls and puts in a large order of cupcakes for later that day. Hassan knows that he won't be able to bake all the cupcakes in time, so he says that he can't help her.

❏ **3.** Lana is a customer service representative. She is getting a lot of calls about a problem with one of her company's products. However, she must spend up to 20 minutes on each call to resolve the problem. To save time, she posts a message on the company's social media page explaining how to solve the problem so customers don't have to call.

❏ **4.** Sam works at a cash register in a small grocery store. The card machine is broken. If a customer doesn't have cash, he says that he's sorry and that an electrician is coming soon to fix the machine.

C ANALYZE. Read the situations in Exercise B again. What are the different ways the people find creative solutions to problems?

❏   **a.** be honest to customers about a problem

❏   **b.** think of an idea that saves time

❏   **c.** ask someone else for help

❏   **d.** follow instructions

❏   **e.** think of a new way to get something done

Unit 6: Getting a Good Deal

Lesson 1: Vocabulary

A Look at the pictures. Complete the sentences. More than one answer is sometimes possible.

| bent | cracked | defective | incompatible | broken | damaged | ~~dented~~ | leaking |

1. The box was ___dented___ when it arrived.

2. The vacuum cleaner is _____.

3. The charger is _____ with my phone.

4. The sink faucet is _____.

5. I sat on my phone. Now it's _____.

6. I dropped the camera. Now it's _____.

7. The TV screen was _____ during delivery.

8. Don't use the iron. It's _____.

B Look at the pictures of the purchases. What is wrong with each one?

| cracked | dented | leaking | defective | incompatible | scratched |

1. The cable is _____.

2. This CD is _____.

3. The faucet is _____.

4. The back of the car is _____.

5. My phone doesn't work.

It's _____.

6. The iron is _____.

C WRITE ABOUT IT. Read the situation. Think about your own experience. Answer the questions.

Sometimes stores sell "refurbished" appliances (used appliances that have been repaired). Refurbished appliances cost a lot less than new appliances. Refurbished appliances usually work well, but they may be scratched or dented. They often have a warranty to fix parts, but the warranty may not last long (for example, 1-3 years). New appliances usually have a longer warranty, but they may cost a lot more.

1. Have you ever bought a refurbished appliance? Was it a good experience?

_____

_____

2. Do you think refurbished appliances and computers are a good deal? Why or why not?

_____

_____

Lessons 2 & 3: Grammar

(A) Read the two sentences. Write one sentence. Use *too* or *either*.

1. The phone is broken. The vacuum cleaner is broken.

The phone is broken, and the vacuum cleaner is, too.

2. My tablet is scratched. My computer screen is scratched.

_____

3. Her camera isn't working. Her LED TV isn't working.

_____

4. Delivery is free. Repairs are free.

_____

5. The treadmill isn't covered under the warranty. The microwave isn't covered under the warranty.

_____

(B) Look at the information. Write sentences about the appliances. Different combinations are possible.

Product	Problem
refrigerator	cracked
soda machine	~~leaking~~
~~faucet~~	not working
washing machine	dented
~~coffeemaker~~	defective
air conditioner	broken
headphones	damaged
treadmill	not compatible with my phone
charger	not covered under warranty

1. *The coffeemaker is leaking, and the faucet is, too.*

2. _____

3. _____

4. _____

5. _____

6. _____

Lesson 4: Reading

A **DEVELOP YOUR ACADEMIC SKILLS. Read the Academic Skill. Look for formatting clues in the article.**

The main points of the article will be about _____.
  a. whether coupons are better than loyalty programs
  b. ways online shopping can save you money
  c. using social media to share shopping tips

B ▶ Listen and read.

ONLINE SHOPPING – WHAT'S THE BIG DEAL?

More and more Americans are choosing to shop online. There are a great many products to choose from. You can make big savings, too! There are three ways people can get greats deals online:

5 • compare prices
  • use coupons and sign up for loyalty programs
  • follow social media

COMPARE A quick search on competing websites can show **instant** savings. It's easy to
10 *compare* how much different sites are charging for the same products. For example, some companies don't charge for *delivery*, and other websites do not charge *sales tax*.

DISCOUNTS Using *coupons* is a good option,
15 too. Sign up for your favorite sites' newsletters. This way, you will get coupons emailed to you directly, or get an **alert** when there is a sale.

Check if the store has a *loyalty program*. This gives you points for every purchase. When you have enough points, you can get a good discount or reward.

SOCIAL MEDIA Using *social media* can help you save money, too. It can be difficult to keep track of all the
20 special offers in your newsfeed. Follow only your favorite brands. You will then get **alerts** when they post about a sale or an offer.

FOCUS Shopping online makes it much easier to find a deal. When you shop in a store, it is easy to get **distracted**. Stores put expensive products at eye level so they are the first things you see. You have to work hard to find the good deals in a store.

25 When you are shopping online, you can *easily search* for a product. Websites often list special offers at the top of the search results. You can then choose the cheapest option.

Shopping online is a great way to save money. All it takes is a little research.

Top seven online shopping categories in the U.S. (2018)

Category	Percentage
Electronics	69%
Books	67%
Clothing	63%
Personal care	58%
Household goods	38%
Office supplies	30%
Food and groceries	20%

Percentage of purchases made online

C **IDENTIFY. What is the main idea of the article? Circle the correct answer.**

  a. There are lots of ways to get a good deal online.
  b. Getting a good deal online can be complicated.
  c. It's easy to get distracted when shopping online.

D CITE EVIDENCE. Complete the sentences. Where is the information? Write the line number.

Lines

1. Comparing different websites for the same products is _____.
   a. a useful way to save money
   b. not worth the effort
   c. too complicated for most people _____

2. Customers can find news about their favorite stores by _____.
   a. asking their friends to follow it
   b. signing up for email and social media updates
   c. reading about it in the newspaper _____

3. Store shoppers are more likely to _____.
   a. hunt for a bargain
   b. compare many different products
   c. buy what they see without thinking _____

E INTERPRET. Complete the sentences about the chart.

1. The difference between the most and the least purchased products is _____.
   a. 49%   b. 59%   c. 69%

2. The percentage of household goods bought is _____ the percentage of food and groceries.
   a. less than double   b. double   c. more than double

3. People are more likely to buy clothing online than _____.
   a. books   b. pens and notebooks   c. printers and cell phones

F INTERPRET VOCABULARY. Complete the sentences.

1. The word *instant* in line 9 means _____.
   a. immediate   b. incredible

2. The word *alert* in line 16 means _____.
   a. wake-up call   b. signal

3. The word *distracted* in line 23 means _____.
   a. unable to focus and think carefully   b. interested in a new product

G SUMMARIZE. What are the most important ideas in the article? Write three sentences.

_____

_____

_____

Lessons 5 & 6: Listening and Grammar

A Look at the cell phone plans. Read the statements. Write *T* (true) or *F* (false).

SUNPHONE

Plan A

300 anytime minutes/month

200 texts/month

4,000 MB data/month

$39.95

Plan B

500 anytime minutes/month

250 texts/month

2,500 MB data/month

$49.95

1. Plan A is cheaper than Plan B. ____

2. Plan A has more anytime minutes than Plan B. ____

3. Plan A gives fewer text messages. ____

4. Plan A has more MB data each month. ____

B Look at the ads. Complete the sentences. Use the correct comparative form of the adjectives.

Porto-Grill

Tabletop

11,000 BTUs gives lots of heat

Easy to clean and carry

$71.99

Backyard Grill

20,000 BTUs

Safety rated

$234.99

1. Backyard Grill is _____ to use than Porto-Grill.
   (safe)

2. Porto-Grill is _____ than Backyard Grill.
   (small)

3. Porto-Grill is _____ than Backyard Grill.
   (expensive)

4. Backyard Grill is _____ than Porto-Grill.
   (heavy)

5. Backyard Grill is _____ to clean than Porto-Grill.
   (difficult)

C Complete the conversation. Use the correct comparative form of the adjectives.

A: Last week I got my new satellite television installed.

B: Wow. Cool!

A: Yeah. I used to have cable, but now I have satellite. The satellite

company had a _____ price than the cable company.
       1. (low)

B: Really?

A: Yes. And I also got a digital video recorder with my new satellite package.

It's _____ than my old cable box.
     2. (convenient)

B: So is it really _____ than cable?
                     3. (good)

A: Absolutely. I'm so much _____ with the satellite company.
                             4. (happy)

D Read the ads. Write sentences. Use the correct comparative form of the adjectives.

Thermos 2000

1.5 cubic feet

1100 watts cooking power

Great for small spaces!

$159

Sun Wave

1.7 cubic feet

1200 watts cooking power

Cooks fast!

$239

1. _The Sun Wave is bigger than the Thermos 2000._ _____ (big)

2. _____ (efficient)

3. _____ (small)

4. _____ (cheap)

Lesson 7: Workplace, Community, and Life Skills

A Look at the rebate information. Write *T* (true) or *F* (false).

Up to $100 Rebate
on any New 4G Smartphone!

Buy a new 4G smartphone between 9/1/20 and 10/31/20, and you could be eligible for a rebate of up to $100*.

*Rebate amount is based on the purchase price of eligible items. Rebate form must be completed online before 11/30/2020 to receive rebate. Rebate will be delivered via bank transfer only. Rebate available for online purchases only.

1. The rebate applies to new 4G smartphones only. ____

2. You must buy the smartphone before 9/1/20 to get the rebate. ____

3. You can get $100 back no matter how much the smartphone costs. ____

4. You cannot receive the rebate in cash. ____

5. You can get the rebate if you buy an eligible phone in-store. ____

B WRITE ABOUT IT. Imagine that you are applying online to get a rebate for a product. Complete the form.

Name _____

Address _____ Apt. _____

City _____ State ____ Zip Code _____

Cell phone _____ Email address _____

Product name _____ Product manufacturer _____

Purchase price _____ Purchase date _____ Store name _____

ADD SCANNED DOCUMENTS HERE

SUBMIT

Lessons 8 & 9: Grammar

A Complete the sentences about the two kitchen appliance stores. Use *as ... as.*

1. Mary's Bath World is _____*as close as*_____ Tile House from here.
   (close)

2. The prices at Mary's Bath World are _____ they are at Tile House.
   (not / low)

3. The appliances at Tile House are _____ the appliances at Mary's Bath
   (not / dependable)

   World.

4. Mary's Bath World is _____ Tile House because it's only open until
   (not / convenient)

   5:00 P.M.

5. Customer service at Mary's Bath World is just _____ Tile House's
   (good)

   service.

B Compare the two ads. Complete the sentences. Use *as . . . as.*

Dirt Angel

2-year warranty
15 lbs.
$99.99

HABER
5-YEAR WARRANTY
25 LBS.
$149.99

1. Dirt Angel _____*is not as heavy as*_____ Haber.
   (not / heavy)

2. Dirt Angel _____ Haber.
   (not / expensive)

3. Haber _____ Dirt Angel.
   (not / cheap)

4. Haber _____ Dirt Angel.
   (not / easy to carry)

C Read the review comparing two stores. Write sentences comparing the experiences at the stores.

Customer Review		
	Abe's Appliances	**Bee's Home Goods**
Customer Service	👍	👎
Prices	👎	👍
Convenient Location	👍	👎
Open Late	👍	👎
Selection	👎	👍

1. (customer service / not / good)

   Bee's customer service is not as good as Abe's.

2. (prices / not / high)

   _____

3. (location / not / convenient)

   _____

4. (store hours / not / good)

   _____

5. (selection / not / wide)

   _____

D Compare the two ads. Complete the sentences. Use *not as . . . as*.

Viza 39" LED TV
1080p resolution full HD
Superfast
60 hertz refresh rate
$349.99

Polara 44" LED TV
4k resolution
$429.99 120 hertz refresh rate

1. _____ (expensive)

2. _____ (big)

3. _____ (fast)

Lesson 10: Writing

A Read the Writing Skill. Read the text. Write *T* (true) or *F* (false).

My brother has a Viza phone, but I have a Polara phone. Each phone has a high-resolution screen, and both have good-quality cameras. However, I prefer my Polara phone. The battery lasts a lot longer, and the screen is much larger, too. The Polara phone is also cheaper than the Viza phone.

> **Writing Skill: Use details to compare and contrast.**
> When you compare two things, you find similarities between them. When you contrast, you find differences. You should organize similarities and differences together in your writing and include supporting details.

1. The Viza phone doesn't have a high-resolution screen. ____

2. The Polara phone's battery is better than the Viza's. ____

3. The Viza phone's camera isn't as good as the Polara's. ____

B Read the text in Exercise A again. Circle the correct answer.

1. What are the two similarities between the Viza phone and the Polara phone?
   a. Long battery life and low price
   b. Large screens and good-quality cameras
   c. High-resolution screens and good-quality cameras

2. What is one of the main differences between the Viza phone and the Polara phone?
   a. The camera quality
   b. The price
   c. The sound quality

C Read the text. Correct four more mistakes.

store

E-Buy and LectroWorld are two electronic stores in my city. Each ~~stores~~ has a well-organized website where you can check the latest offers. There is also a good selection of appliances at both stores, either. However, I prefer to buy my appliances at E-Buy. The rebates at E-Buy are usually more good, and the delivery charges are as cheaper, too. The custumer service at LectroWorld isn't good as E-Buy. The store doesn't offer free returns, too.

Lesson 11: Soft Skills at Work

Ⓐ UNDERSTAND. Complete the sentence.

A person who responds to customer needs _____.
    a. helps to solve a customer's problem
    b. asks a manager for help
    c. tells the customer what went wrong

Ⓑ IDENTIFY. Read the conversations at work. In which conversations does the person respond to customer needs? Check (✓) the conversations.

❑ **1. Customer:** Excuse me. I bought a new phone here last week but I want to change the plan. It's a lot more expensive than my old plan.

    Maxim: That's no problem. I can offer you a cheaper plan. However, for the same price, we could also offer you unlimited texts and data.

    Customer: OK. Unlimited data sounds like a good deal.

❑ **2. Customer:** Hello, I'm looking for a new digital camera, but it's hard to know which one has the best quality. Is this one as good as that one?

    Ayla: Well, why don't you take a few photos here in the store with each one? Look at the photos on the camera. I can show you each photo on a large TV screen, too. You can then see them more clearly.

❑ **3. Customer:** Hi, I had a TV delivered to my house yesterday, but the power cord is damaged. It won't turn on! I'd like to return it and get a full refund.

    Diya: I'm sorry to hear that. However, you don't need to return it. We can send a technician to replace the cord. It's free of charge, too.

Ⓒ ANALYZE. Read the conversations in Exercise B again. What are the different ways the people respond to customer needs?

❑   **a.** let them try out a product before buying it

❑   **b.** offer a different type of service or product

❑   **c.** explain the warranty conditions

❑   **d.** offer to repair something free of charge

❑   **e.** be honest if they're unable to solve a problem

Lesson 1: Vocabulary

A Match the words and phrases with the pictures.

| highway | construction | traffic jam | toll booth | tow truck | vehicle |

1. _____

2. _____

3. _____

4. _____

5. _____

6. _____

B Complete the sentences.

| overpass | construction | lanes | exit | traffic jam |

1. Cars can use an _____ to cross to the other side of a freeway.

2. I think that there's _____ on the highway for the next two weeks.

3. There's a big _____ on the freeway because of the accident.

4. Remember to signal when you change _____.

5. The _____ is closed because of construction, so take the next one.

C Look at the underlined words. Circle the words with the closest meaning.

1. There are so many <u>vehicles</u> on the road today!
   a. people
   b. cars and trucks
   c. construction workers

2. There's heavy traffic on the freeway because of road <u>construction</u>.
   a. building and repairs
   b. blocked entrance
   c. moving vehicles

3. Keep going north on the <u>freeway</u> for 30 more miles.
   a. road with entrance and exit ramps
   b. toll road with toll booth
   c. city street

4. Pull off to the <u>shoulder</u> if you're having trouble seeing the road.
   a. left lane
   b. middle of the road
   c. right edge of the road

5. The <u>overpass</u> looks crowded. Let's not take that exit.
   a. a very busy highway
   b. bridge near a freeway
   c. a structure like a bridge that allows one road to go over another road

D What do you do when you are stuck in traffic as the driver or a passenger? Write at least three things.

I listen to the radio.

_____

_____

_____

Lessons 2 & 3: Grammar

A Complete the sentences. Use *a*, *an*, or *the*.

1. I need _____ oil change.

2. I saw _____ new car I like.

3. I like the color of _____ seats.

4. _____ air filter is dirty.

5. I need _____ new battery.

6. _____ engine is making a funny noise.

B Complete the conversation. Use *a*, *an*, or *the*.

A: I was in **(1.)** _____ accident last week!

B: Oh no! I'm sorry to hear that!

A: It's OK. It was just **(2.)** _____ small accident. No one was hurt. But my car has **(3.)** _____ dent in the rear bumper. I have **(4.)** _____ appointment with my auto insurance agent next Monday.

B: Will you get **(5.)** _____ dent fixed?

A: I hope so!

B: I'm sure **(6.)** _____ insurance agent can help you.

C Imagine you are a mechanic. Tell customers about their car problems. Write sentences. Add *a*, *an*, or *the*.

1. (replace / you need to / brakes)

   You need to replace the brakes.

2. (has / oil leak / your car)

   _____

3. (air filter / you need to / clean)

   _____

4. (you need to / fan belt / change)

   _____

5. (get / new tire / you need to)

   _____

Lesson 4: Workplace, Life, and Community Skills

A Look at the picture. Write the parts of the car.

| engine | headlights | hood | trunk | windshield | sideview mirror |

1. _____   2. _____

3. _____   4. _____

5. _____   6. _____

B Complete the sentences. Use the words and phrases from Exercise A. Some words may be used more than once.

1. The car needs a new _____*windshield*_____ wiper.

2. If the _____ won't start, try waiting five minutes before you start the car again.

3. You can put groceries in the back seat or in the _____ of the car.

4. Your _____ are out. You should change the bulbs.

5. Turn on your _____ wipers when it rains or snows.

6. When you need to check the engine, open the _____.

C Look at the picture. Write the parts of the car.

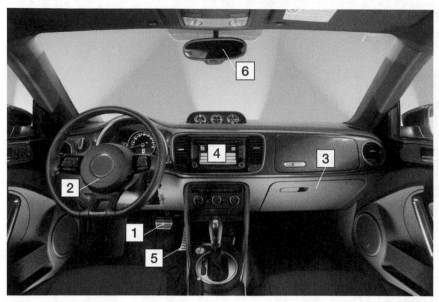

horn	brake pedal	glove compartment
GPS	rearview mirror	accelerator/gas pedal

1. _____

2. _____

3. _____

4. _____

5. _____

6. _____

D Complete the sentences. Use words and phrases from Exercise C. Not all of them will be used.

1. Use the _____ to find your way to a new destination

2. Press down on the _____ to increase speed.

3. When you change lanes, look in your _____, and check for traffic behind you.

4. Make sure to check your _____ after driving through a lot of water.

E WRITE ABOUT IT. All types of cars use similar dashboard icons. Look up dashboard icons online. Draw three icons that you haven't already learned. Write a sentence about what each one means.

	_____
	_____
	_____

Lessons 5 & 6: Grammar

A Put the words in the correct order.

1. (talking / the man / on a cell phone / was)

_____

2. (watching / the drivers / the road / weren't)

_____

3. (the passengers / wearing / seat belts / weren't)

_____

B Complete the paragraph. Use the past continuous.

I _____ TV when I heard a loud crash outside. I went outside. Two
      1. (watch)

police officers _____ the drivers. While the drivers
      2. (interview)

_____, the police asked me if I had seen the accident. I told the police
      3. (wait)

I _____ at home when the accident happened. The police asked more
      4. (sit)

witnesses. One man saw the accident. He said the first driver _____
      5. (not / pay attention)

when she hit the other car.

C Look at the pictures. What were the drivers doing wrong? Use the past continuous.

_____   _____   _____

_____   _____   _____

D Complete the email. Use the past continuous and the words in parentheses.

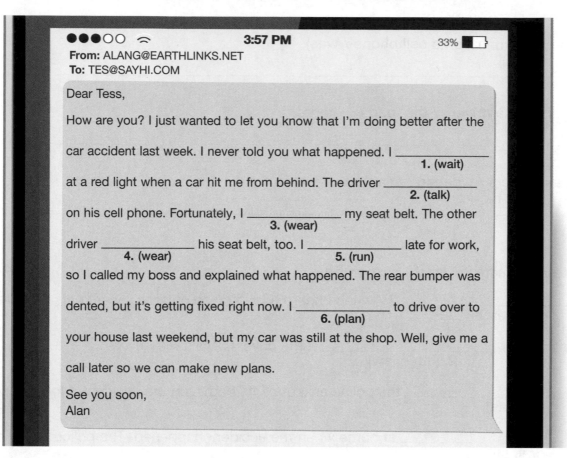

○○●○○ 🛜   **3:57 PM**   33% ▮▮

From: ALANG@EARTHLINKS.NET
To: TES@SAYHI.COM

Dear Tess,

How are you? I just wanted to let you know that I'm doing better after the

car accident last week. I never told you what happened. I _____
                                                              1. (wait)

at a red light when a car hit me from behind. The driver _____
                                                                2. (talk)

on his cell phone. Fortunately, I _____ my seat belt. The other
                                                3. (wear)

driver _____ his seat belt, too. I _____ late for work,
       4. (wear)   **5. (run)**

so I called my boss and explained what happened. The rear bumper was

dented, but it's getting fixed right now. I _____ to drive over to
                                                           6. (plan)

your house last weekend, but my car was still at the shop. Well, give me a

call later so we can make new plans.

See you soon,
Alan

E Rewrite the sentences. Use the past continuous.

1. I sit in my car.

    I was sitting in my car.

2. The radio plays.

_____

3. My cell phone rings.

_____

4. The mechanics fix my car.

_____

5. You look at the rearview mirror.

_____

Lesson 7: Reading

A DEVELOP YOUR ACADEMIC SKILLS. Read the Academic Skill. Look at the chart with the text.

The topic of the text will be _____.
    a. road accidents in the U.S.
    b. road deaths in the U.S.
    c. the number of crashes in the U.S.

> **Academic Skill: Interpret charts**
>
> Charts show important information in an article. They show this information in a visual format that is easy to see and understand.

B ▶ Listen and read.

CAR ACCIDENTS IN THE U.S.

Car accidents are very common in the U.S. In fact, thousands of people are killed on the road each year. It's important to know the top reasons why crashes happen. This can help you stay alert on the road and drive more safely.

5 **DON'T LOSE FOCUS!**
Drivers who are **distracted** are more likely to crash. Some drivers make calls or send text messages while behind the wheels. Others eat lunch while driving or put on makeup when they stop at a red light.

10 Even loud music or a conversation with a passenger can be dangerous. All these things can take your attention off the road.

DON'T DRINK AND DRIVE!
Every day, 29 people in the U.S. die because of drivers who have been drinking. This is one death every 50 minutes!

15 Drinking alcohol and driving is a bad idea. Alcohol **impairs** your judgment and slows down your reaction time. If you are tired, the effects are worse.

DON'T DRIVE TOO FAST!
Speeding is another cause of car accidents. In 2018, more than a quarter of all traffic deaths were caused by speeding. Speed limits are there to protect all road users. Driving within the speed limit gives you enough time to
20 brake if you need to stop suddenly.

DON'T FORGET TO STOP!
Drivers who don't obey a stop sign cause accidents. Stop signs are used at busy junctions, such as crossroads. Drivers must slow down, prepare to stop, and check for other traffic on the road. Drivers should yield, or give way, to traffic from the right. Even if roads seem empty, there is never a reason to ignore a stop sign.

25 **DON'T FORGET SAFETY!**
Dangerous driving causes a huge number of car accidents. Some drivers are **aggressive**, swerve in and out of traffic, or drive too close to the car in front of them. These types of behavior are known as "reckless driving." Don't forget your manners after you step into your car.

If you follow these steps, you can avoid the top driving risks. Driving with care and attention makes the road a
30 nicer place for all users.

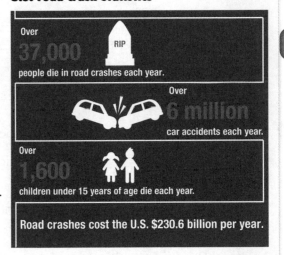

U.S. road crash statistics

Over
37,000
people die in road crashes each year.

Over
6 million
car accidents each year.

Over
1,600
children under 15 years of age die each year.

Road crashes cost the U.S. $230.6 billion per year.

C IDENTIFY. What is the main idea of the article? Circle the correct answer.

    a. Ways to avoid car accidents
    b. Ways to avoid speeding tickets
    c. Ways to spend less money on gas

D CITE EVIDENCE. Complete the sentences. Where is the information? Write the line number.

Lines

1. Many car accidents are caused by drivers who are _____ while driving.
    a. checking the rearview mirror   **b.** not paying attention
    c. using the wrong turn signal _____

2. In 2018, _____ of all traffic deaths were caused by speeding.
    a. more than 25%   **b.** more than 40%   **c.** more than 50% _____

3. Driving slowly means a driver _____.
    a. has more time to react   **b.** gets stuck in traffic
    c. won't ignore a red light _____

E INTERPRET. Complete the sentences about the infographic.

1. More than _____ million car accidents happen in the U.S. every year.
    a. 5   **b.** 6   **c.** 7

2. More than _____ thousand people are killed each year in road accidents in the U.S.
    a. 36   **b.** 37   **c.** 38

3. The U.S. suffers a damage of more than _____ billion dollars each year because of road crashes.
    a. 231.5   **b.** 230.5   **c.** 230.6

F INTERPRET VOCABULARY. Complete the sentences.

1. The word *distracted* in line 6 means _____
    a. not paying attention   **b.** using a cellphone

2. The word *impairs* in line 15 means _____
    a. improves   **b.** makes worse

3. The word *aggressive* in line 26 means _____
    a. not skillful   **b.** forceful

G SUMMARIZE. What are the most important ideas in the article? Write three sentences.

_____

_____

_____

Lesson 8: Writing

A Read the Writing Skill. Write the opinions of each driver. Give a supporting sentence for each opinion.

Yesterday, I took a taxi to a work meeting. When we arrived at the office, the taxi driver started to park. Suddenly, I heard a loud crash. The taxi had hit an SUV when it was backing up into a parking space.

> **Writing Skill: Present two different opinions when arguing**
> Argue for or against something by presenting two different opinions. Then clearly state which opinion is yours. Support your opinion with reasons.

The taxi driver jumped out of the car. He was very angry. He said, "Your car is parked too far out into the road!" The SUV driver was angry, too. He said, "I parked correctly! Look! My car is within the line." He asked for the taxi driver's insurance information.

I think the accident was the taxi driver's fault. He was listening to loud music and singing. I think he forgot to check the rearview mirror before he parked.

1. Taxi driver's opinion: _____

   Supporting sentence: _____

2. SUV driver's opinion: _____

   Supporting sentence: _____

B Match each opinion with its reason. Which one is the writer's opinion? Circle the number.

1. The accident was the writer's fault ____   **a.** because he was not paying attention.

2. The accident was the taxi driver's fault ____   **b.** because he had parked badly.

3. The accident was the SUV driver's fault ____   **c.** because he was late for the meeting.

C Read the text. Correct five more mistakes.

Traffic was slow ~~in~~ *on* the way to work this morning. Drivers were getting impatient. A hybrid crashes into the sedan in front of it. The woman driving a hybrid said, "You need to move off more quickly!" The man in the sedan says, "You wasn't paying attention! You need to wait for my car to move before you drive." I think the driver of the hybrid was at fault. When she got out of the car, she was rubbed her eyes. I think she was too tired to concentrate on driving.

Lessons 9 & 10: Grammar

A Match the beginning of each sentence with the correct ending. Write the letters.

1. When you register your vehicle, _e_   **a.** check the internet for deals.

2. Before a mechanic works on your car, ___   **b.** you spend a lot of time on the road.

3. Before you buy a car, ___   **c.** make sure the gas cap is on.

4. When you drive for a living, ___   **d.** ask for an estimate.

5. After you get gas, ___   **e.** you might have to get a pollution test.

B Write the words in the correct order. Add commas where necessary. More than one order is possible.

1. (buy a car / you / to have / you / insurance / when / need)

_____

2. (all the costs / to understand / before / you / need / sign the contract / you)

_____

3. (from the car dealership / drive it home / you / when / loses value / your car)

_____

4. (you / need / for pedestrians / drive in town / when / to look out / you)

_____

C Rewrite each tip as one sentence. More than one answer is possible.

1. You drive. Look around to be safe. **(when)**

   When you drive, look around to be safe.

2. You turn. Check that no one is in your way. **(before)**

   _____

3. You change lanes. Look over your shoulder. **(before)**

   _____

4. You get in a car. Put on a seat belt. **(after)**

   _____

5. You buy insurance. You need to understand the coverage. **(when)**

   _____

Lesson 11: Soft Skills at Work

A UNDERSTAND. Complete the sentence. Circle the correct answer.

A person who is flexible at work _____.
- **a.** likes to have the same routine every day
- **b.** adapts to situations and likes to learn new things
- **c.** knows the best way of doing things

B IDENTIFY. Read the conversations at work. In which conversations are the people flexible? Check (✓) the conversations.

❑ **1. Customer:** Hi, we're going downtown. Wait, do you have a car seat for my son?

   Driver: No, my booking was for two adults. Is your son coming, too?

   Customer: Yes, our plans changed at the last minute.

   Driver: Okay. Let me call my co-worker. He is on a job nearby and keeps a spare seat in his trunk.

❑ **2. Supervisor:** Pete, this is Max. He'll be working with you today.

   Pete: Nice to meet you, Max! Before we start, what shall I have him help with?

   Supervisor: Max doesn't have much experience. Can you show him how to do an oil change?

   Pete: Of course. I've never trained anyone before but I'll do my best. We'll both be learning new things together, Max!

❑ **3. Sara:** I was learning about new accounting software at that course last weekend. It sounded good.

   Bo: Oh, really? I'm happy with the software we use now.

   Sara: Yeah, maybe you're right. It was kind of hard. We should stick with what we know.

   Bo: I think so. Learning how to use new software would waste a lot of time.

C ANALYZE. Read the conversations in Exercise B again. What are the different ways the people are flexible?

❑ **a.** learn a new skill

❑ **b.** do tasks they know well

❑ **c.** adapt to a situation

❑ **d.** see change as a good thing

❑ **e.** take on a challenge

Unit 8: Staying Healthy

Lesson 1: Vocabulary

A Match the pictures with the phrases. Write the letters.

a.

b.

c.

d.

e.

f.

1. eat fast food   _e_

2. buy fresh fruits and vegetables   ___

3. drink sugary beverages   ___

4. have a snack   ___

5. buy frozen dinners   ___

6. cook homemade meals   ___

B Complete the sentences with the phrases from Exercise A. Not all phrases will be used.

1. When you want to _____, try a piece of fruit instead of candy or chips.

2. It's OK to _____ once in a while, but don't drink them every day!

3. At the grocery store, you should _____.

4. It can take more time to _____, but it's healthier than getting takeout.

C Complete the paragraph. Use the words in the box.

buy fresh fruits and vegetables	frozen dinners	sugary
cook homemade meals	fast food	takeout

It's very easy to have bad eating habits and make poor food choices. Everywhere you look, you see **(1.)** _____ restaurants. Many people work long hours, so at the end of the day, they just get **(2.)** _____ because they don't want to take the time to **(3.)** _____. It's important to remember that our bodies need good food to stay healthy. Go to the produce section of your grocery store and **(4.)** _____. Stay away from **(5.)** _____ beverages and drink water instead. Don't buy **(6.)** _____ because they usually have a lot of sodium. If you make small changes to your eating habits, you can live a long and healthy life!

D WRITE ABOUT IT. Do you have healthy or unhealthy eating habits? Write sentences about your eating habits.

I like to cook homemade meals. I think homemade meals are healthier than fast food or takeout.

_____

_____

_____

_____

_____

Lessons 2 & 3: Grammar

A Read the sentences. Cross out the incorrect form of the superlative.

1. For many busy people, eating fast food is the ~~most quick~~ / **quickest** option.

2. Mondays are the **most busy** / **busiest** day of the week for David.

3. Avoiding fatty foods was one of the **hardest** / **most hard** things Hector has ever done.

4. This is one of the **more interesting** / **most interesting** books about healthy eating I've read this year.

5. Fatima is always smiling. She is the **happiest** / **most happy** person I know.

B Complete the sentences. Use superlatives.

1. What is _____*the fastest*_____ way to the grocery store?
       (fast)

2. This is _____ restaurant I've ever been to! The cheapest starter costs $20.
            (expensive)

3. I stopped drinking sugary drinks a year ago. It was one of _____ things
                                                                  (difficult)

   I've ever done.

4. You should use food storage bags. It's _____ way to keep food fresh.
                                              (good)

5. Maria's brother exercises every day and never eats fast food. He's one of

   _____ people I know.
          (healthy)

6. That seafood dish is one of _____ items on the menu. I just love it!
                                   (delicious)

C WRITE ABOUT IT. What is the most expensive thing you have eaten in a restaurant? What is the most delicious thing you have ever eaten? Use superlatives. Write three lines.

The most expensive thing I have ever eaten in a restaurant was a huge steak!

_____

_____

_____

Lesson 4: Workplace, Life, and Community Skills

A Look at the two snack bar labels. Complete the sentences with information from the labels.

Yogurt Protein Bar

Nutrition Facts
Serving Size 1 bar

Amount Per Serving

Calories 140	Calories from Fat 30

	% Daily Value *
Total Fat 3.5g	5%
Saturated Fat 2g	10%
Trans Fat 0g	
Cholesterol 0mg	0%
Sodium 110mg	5%
Total Carbohydrate 26g	9%
Dietary Fiber 1g	4%
Sugars 13g	
Protein 2g	4%
Calcium	20%
Iron	2%

INGREDIENTS: WHEAT, WHEY AND LOWFAT BUTTERMILK, SALT, CORN OIL. CONTAINS DAIRY INGREDIENTS.

Est. Percent of Calories from:
Fat 22.5% Carbs 74.3%
Protein 5.7%

Spring Valley Peanut Bar

Nutrition Facts
Serving Size 1 bar

Amount Per Serving

Calories 180	Calories from Fat 50

	% Daily Value *
Total Fat 6g	9%
Saturated Fat 0.5g	2%
Cholesterol 0mg	0%
Sodium 160mg	7%
Total Carbohydrate 29g	10%
Dietary Fiber 2g	8%
Sugars 11g	
Protein 4g	8%
Calcium	20%
Iron	2%

INGREDIENTS: WHEAT, RICE, PEANUTS, HONEY, SUNFLOWER OIL.

Est. Percent of Calories from:
Fat 30.0% Carbs 64.4%
Protein 8.9%

1. There are _____ grams of saturated fat in the Yogurt Protein Bar and _____ grams of saturated fat in Spring Valley Peanut Bar.

2. There are more calories from fat in the _____ Bar.

3. The _____ Bar has less sodium than the _____ Bar.

4. There are _____ grams of sugar in the Yogurt Protein Bar and _____ grams of sugar in the Spring Valley Peanut Bar.

5. The Spring Valley Peanut Bar has _____ more grams of protein than the Yogurt Protein Bar.

B Read the situations. Which snack from Exercise A can each person eat? Check (✓) each one.

Situation	Yogurt Protein Bar	Spring Valley Peanut Bar	Neither
1. Ahmed has high blood pressure. He needs to avoid salt.			
2. Tim is allergic to milk.			
3. Sam needs to cut the amount of fat in his diet.			
4. Mark is allergic to peanuts.			
5. Ana has Type 2 diabetes. She should not have any sugar.			

C WRITE ABOUT IT. Find the nutritional information online for three snacks that you like to eat. Use values per 100g. Complete the table below. Which is the least healthy snack? Explain why.

Snack	Calories	Total fat	Total sugars	Protein

_____

_____

_____

Lessons 5 & 6: Grammar

A Put the words in the correct order. More than one answer is sometimes possible.

1. (like / at the movies / eating / candy bars / they)

   _____

2. (juice / in the morning / drinking / he / enjoys)

   _____

3. (doesn't mind / she / early / waking up)

   _____

4. (after work / like / basketball / playing / we)

   _____

5. (on the weekends / enjoy / we / takeout / eating)

   _____

B Complete the paragraph. Use the gerund form of the verbs in the box.

| ~~do~~ | diet | drink | eat | take | vacuum |

1. Jeffrey enjoys __*doing*__ tai chi because he likes to exercise.

2. Try _____ water instead of soda.

3. Stop _____ junk food if you want to lose weight.

4. These days, doctors do not recommend _____. Instead they tell patients to have good eating habits, exercise, and control portions.

5. Try _____ at least 20 minutes a day to exercise.

6. Consider _____ or doing other housework for exercise.

C Complete the paragraph. Use gerunds and the verbs in parentheses.

Ricardo is 43 years old and lives in Los Angeles. He has Type 2 diabetes. His doctor told him

he has to _____ *stop eating* _____ junk food and change his lifestyle. He also told
　　　　　　　　1. (stop / eat)

Ricardo that he needs to _____ every day. He suggested running,
　　　　　　　　　　　　　2. (start / exercise)

swimming, walking, or playing soccer. Ricardo _____, and he
　　　　　　　　　　　　　　　　　　　　　　　3. (not / enjoy / run)

_____ . But he _____ for walks. His wife goes
　　4. (not / like / swim)　　　　　　　　**5. (not / mind / go)**

out with him, and they walk around the park three times a week. Ricardo has also changed his

eating habits. Now he shops with his wife, and they buy more fruits and vegetables. They

cook more homemade meals and buy less takeout food. They also

_____ healthier meals for the family.
　6. (spend time / plan)

D Read the situations. Write tips for a healthy lifestyle. Use the words in parentheses and gerunds. Start the sentences with *consider*, *think about*, or *try*.

1. My husband eats too much.
(**cook / smaller meals**)

　Think about cooking smaller meals.　　　　　　　　　　　　　　　

2. My children love eating chips and drinking soda.
(**give / them / fruits and vegetables**)

　_____

3. I have a bad habit of getting takeout all the time.
(**prepare / homemade meals**)

　_____

4. My children like watching TV for hours every day.
(**increase / their physical activity**)

　_____

A Listen and read.

USING APPS TO CHANGE YOUR DIET

In the U.S., about 36.5 percent of adults are **obese**. Unfortunately, some of the biggest health problems in the U.S. are caused by being overweight. Many people don't realize that the food they're eating is unhealthy for them.

5 However, people might be able to change this with the help of technology. Nowadays, apps can give you a lot of great information about food. They can also support you if you want to change your diet. Here are some ways food apps can help.

10 **COUNT CALORIES**
In general, avoid having more than 2,000 calories a day. Eating more than that can make you overweight. One of the easiest ways of staying under this limit is to use an app to count calories. Every time you have a snack, meal, or drink,

15 add it to your daily food **log**. The app can find out how many calories each one contains. At the end of the day, the app will tell you your total daily calories. Some apps also let you scan a food product's **barcode**. These can also tell you if a product is high or low in calories.

PLAN YOUR MEALS
Imagine you're on a diet. You need to reduce the amount of carbohydrates you eat. If you cut out things like

20 potatoes, rice, and pasta, how do you know if you're getting all the nutrition you need? Luckily, apps can help you with this, too. In some apps, you can enter the type of diet you are on. They can then give you delicious and nutritious recipes, but without the types of food you should avoid.

FIND A COMMUNITY
Many apps let you join communities of people who are also trying to become healthier. This is one of the best

25 ways to stay on your diet. Other people can give you useful recipe tips. They can also give you support when you need it the most.

There are lots of different food apps. It's important to choose the right one. Using the right app can help you to lose weight and to stay healthy.

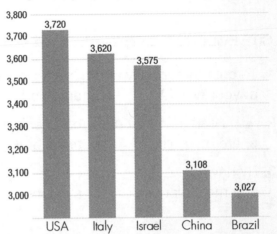

Daily calories intake around the world (2017)

Country	Calories
USA	3,720
Italy	3,620
Israel	3,575
China	3,108
Brazil	3,027

B DEVELOP YOUR ACADEMIC SKILLS. Read the Academic Skill. Answer the question.

Which of the following statements is a fact?
- **a.** "In the U.S., about 36.5 percent of adults are obese."
- **b.** "However, people might be able to change this if they use the right technology."
- **c.** "Nowadays, apps can give you a lot of great information about food."

Academic Skill: Understand facts and opinions

When you read, look carefully at the information. Is it a fact (something you can prove) or an opinion (a person's idea or belief)? Identifying facts and opinions when you read helps you make better judgments about what you are reading.

C IDENTIFY. What is the main idea of the article?

    a. People don't eat enough fruits and vegetables.
    b. Apps can help you improve your diet.
    c. Many foods are very high in calories.

D CITE EVIDENCE. Complete the sentences. Where is the information? Write the line number.

Lines

1. To count your daily number of calories, add _____ to your log.
    a. your weight   **b.** any food and drink you have   **c.** 2,000 calories   _____

2. Apps can help you plan your meals if you _____.
    a. are on a diet   **b.** are allergic to some ingredients   **c.** don't like pasta   _____

3. By having _____, you can get support as well as new ideas for recipes.
    a. a meal planner   **b.** a calorie counter   **c.** an online community   _____

E INTERPRET. Complete the sentences about the chart.

1. The country where people take in the fewest number of calories per day is _____.
    a. Israel   **b.** China   **c.** Brazil

2. In _____, people have an average of 3,575 calories a day.
    a. the U.S.   **b.** Israel   **c.** China

3. People in _____ take in more calories than people in Israel do.
    a. Italy   **b.** China   **c.** Brazil

F INTERPRET VOCABULARY. Complete the sentences.

1. The word *obese* in line 1 means _____.
    a. overweight   **b.** healthy

2. The word *log* in line 15 means _____.
    a. a type of diary   **b.** a type of recipe

3. The word *barcode* in line 16 means _____.
    a. a pleasant design on a product packaging
    b. a packaging label that gives you product information

G SUMMARIZE. What are the most important ideas in the article? Write three sentences.

_____

_____

_____

Lesson 8 & 9: Grammar

A Put the words in the correct order.

1. (to the dentist / going / for young children / can be scary)

   _____

2. (your teeth / regularly / is good / flossing / for your dental health)

   _____

3. (is / important / after / brushing / every meal)

   _____

4. (sugary / eating / food / for teeth / not / is / good)

   _____

5. (milk / strong / can / keep / drinking / your teeth / help)

   _____

B Rewrite the sentences. Start each sentence with a gerund.

1. It's a good idea to see your dentist at least twice a year.

   Seeing your dentist at least twice a year is a good idea.

2. It's important to floss every night before bed.

   _____

3. It's hard to remember to floss every day.

   _____

4. It's bad for your teeth to drink a lot of sugary beverages.

   _____

5. It's a good idea to go to the dentist if you feel any pain in your teeth or gums.

   _____

Lesson 10: Writing

A Read the Writing Skill. Read the text. Answer the question.

<u>Sugary drinks</u>

Drinking too many sugary beverages is bad for your health. One of the worst drinks you can buy is soda. In a typical can of soda, there can be as much as 39g of sugar. This sugar can make you gain weight. Gaining too much weight can then cause lots of health problems, such as Type 2 diabetes. Drinking sugary drinks may also damage your teeth. Sugar causes cavities. If you like drinking soda, try making a smoothie instead. It is sweet, but it has much less sugar.

> **Writing Skill: Support an opinion with facts**
>
> When you state an opinion, support your opinion with facts. Do research to find facts that support your opinion.

What is the author's main opinion?
- **a.** Sugary drinks are unhealthy.
- **b.** Soda drinks can cause Type 2 diabetes.
- **c.** There is a lot of sugar in a can of soda.

B Read the text in Exercise A again. Look for the facts. Write *T* (true) or *F* (false).

1. Most cans of soda have much more than 39g of sugar. _____

2. If you drink too many sugary drinks, there's a risk of getting Type 2 diabetes. _____

3. Sugary beverages may give you cavities. _____

4. A smoothie usually has more sugar than a can of soda. _____

C Read the text. Correct four more mistakes.

Being

~~Be~~ on a diet can be difficult. One of the good ways to change your diet is to have healthy substitutes of the things you like to eat and drink. For example, if you like whole fat milk, trying drinking low-fat milk instead. Avoid fast food and takeout is also important. If you like takeout food, think about to cook it yourself. There are lots of different recipes online. If you don't have much time, look for the quicker recipe you can cook.

Lesson 11: Soft Skills at Work

A UNDERSTAND. Complete the sentence. Circle the correct answer

A person who takes initiative _____.
   a. waits for a manager to help
   b. does something without being asked
   c. listens to customers' problems

B IDENTIFY. Read the situations at work. In which situations do the people take initiative? Check (✓) the situations.

❑ **1.** Carlos is a server in a new café. He knows that nowadays a lot of people enjoy having organic food options for lunch. He puts a sign outside the door of the café to let people know about the different organic options available.

❑ **2.** Ana is giving a presentation at 3:00 P.M., and she thinks her manager will disagree with a lot of her ideas. Before her meeting, she thinks about why he might object to her ideas and writes down different reasons why her ideas will actually work.

❑ **3.** Ahmet is a cleaner in a factory. He knows that health and safety inspectors are going to visit the factory that afternoon. He can see that the floor is very wet in one of the work areas. He's not sure whether he should clean it up because he's already busy stocking the shelves. Plus, his manager didn't ask him to.

❑ **4.** Sunita works in a customer service department. Her manager sends her an email about a defect that has been found in one of the company's products. She quickly goes onto the company's social media page and explains what the product defect is and how to fix it.

C ANALYZE. Read the situations in Exercise B again. What are the different ways the people take initiative?

❑   **a.** wait for co-workers to solve a problem

❑   **b.** think about and respond to different possible opinions

❑   **c.** make sure that an action is approved before doing anything

❑   **d.** identify a problem and take action before it gets worse

❑   **e.** understand and prepare for what customers might want

Unit 9: Doing Your Job

Lesson 1: Vocabulary

A Match the phrases with the definitions. Write the correct letter.

1. be part of a team ___
2. attend a training session ___
3. discuss a problem ___
4. follow instructions ___

a. talk about something that needs to be fixed
b. work with others
c. listen carefully and do a task correctly
d. take a class or seminar

B Complete each sentence. Circle the correct answer.

1. Teresa loves to learn new skills. She enjoys _____.

   a. giving instructions

   b. attending training sessions

   c. following instructions

2. My manager communicates very clearly. He is good at _____.

   a. following instructions

   b. being responsible

   c. giving instructions

3. Sandra is good with customer problems. She knows how to _____.

   a. train other employees

   b. deal with complaints

   c. attend a training session

4. I never know how I'm doing at work. I wish my supervisor would _____.

   a. give me feedback

   b. train other employees

   c. be responsible for something

C Label the pictures. Use the phrases in the box.

attend a training session   deal with complaints
be part of a team   train other employees

1. _____

2. _____

3. _____

4. _____

D Complete the paragraph. Use the phrases from Exercise C.

Kate was recently promoted to manager at Big John's Pizza Palace. In her new job, she must

(1.) _____. She shows them how to use the cash register, take

orders, and provide customer service. She must also (2.) _____

from customers. Sometimes it's hard, but she enjoys it because she wants to make customers

happy. Next month, she will (3.) _____ to learn about management

skills. Kate is excited to be a manager, but she understands that the manager's job is not only

giving instructions. It also means knowing how to work well with the employees and to

(4.) _____.

E WRITE ABOUT IT. What are your job skills? Write as many of them as you can.

I'm good at training other employees because I like to teach.

_____

_____

_____

Lessons 2 & 3: Grammar

A Replace the underlined words. Use *one* or *ones*.

1. This table is dirty. Can I sit at another <u>table</u>? *(one)*

2. These pens don't work well. Can we get some new <u>pens</u>?

3. Please don't move this desk. Move that <u>desk</u>.

4. The customer called about a vacuum, but the <u>vacuum</u> she wanted was out of stock.

5. We unpacked some boxes, but we unpacked the wrong <u>boxes.</u>

B Complete the conversation between a server and a customer. Use *one* or *ones*.

A: How's everything?

B: The food is great. But I need a fork.

A: Sure. I'll get you **(1.)** _____ and be right back. And would you like dessert?
We have three different pies — apple, mango, and banana cream.

B: Hmm... I like all three. Which **(2.)** _____ do you like the most?

A: Definitely apple.

B: OK, I'll have that **(3.)** _____ then.

A: Will there be anything else?

B: How much are those cookies?

A: The **(4.)** _____ in the jar? Two dollars each.

B: Hmm. Could you give me **(5.)** _____ ? I'll take it home with me.

C Find and correct four mistakes in the conversation.

A: Hi. Can I see that camera, please?

B: Which ones?

A: Those one. The silver ones.

B: Here you go.

A: It's nice. How much is it?

B: For that one? It's $129.99.

A: Hmm. Do you have a cheaper one?

B: Yes. In that case over there we have a discounted ones.

Lesson 4: Reading

A DEVELOP YOUR ACADEMIC SKILLS. Read the Academic Skill. Skim the article. Complete the sentence.

The article will be about _____.
   a. average travel times to work
   b. the different methods of commuting to work
   c. the different costs of driving a car

B ▶ Listen and read.

COMMUTING TO WORK

You can commute to work in lots of different ways. These include driving, public transportation, cycling, and walking. In this article, we discuss the advantages (A) and the disadvantages (D) of each one.

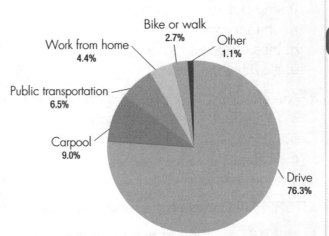

How Americans commute to work (2018)

5 **DRIVING**
   (A) Driving is usually the quickest way of getting to work. You also don't have to follow a strict public transportation **timetable**.

   (D) Sometimes, traffic can make you late for work.
10   Driving can also be expensive. Car **maintenance** can cost a lot of money. If you live far from work, gas can cost of a lot of money, too.

PUBLIC TRANSPORTATION
   (A) Taking public transportation is not as expensive as driving. You don't have to worry about finding a parking
15   space, either. If you take a train or a bus, you also have more free time to read or study before work.

   (D) Like driving, there can sometimes be delays if a bus or a train breaks down. Buses, trains, and subways are also often **overcrowded** in mornings and evenings.

CYCLING
   (A) Cycling is good exercise. It is one of the healthiest ways of commuting to work. It is also one of the cheapest
20   ways of getting to your workplace. In addition, you don't have to worry about timetables or getting stuck in traffic.

   (D) The main disadvantage of cycling is the weather. It can be difficult to ride a bike on cold, rainy, or windy days. Sometimes, it can be dangerous to ride on busy streets, too. It is also not the best option if you live far from your workplace.

25 **WALKING**
   (A) Like cycling, walking is a good exercise. It's free and is better for the environment. It's also the least stressful way of getting to work.

   (D) Walking is very slow. It's definitely not an option if you live far from your workplace. Bad weather may also be a problem.

30 Each method of commuting has its advantages and disadvantages. Which one do you prefer?

C IDENTIFY. What is the main idea of the article?

    a. There are advantages and disadvantages to each method of commuting.
    b. Taking public transportation is much better than driving to work.
    c. If you want to get some exercise on your way to work, you should bike or walk.

D CITE EVIDENCE. Complete the sentences. Where is the information? Write the line number.

                                                                        Lines

1. When you drive to work, you don't have to worry about _____.
    a. the cost of gas
    b. public transportation timetables
    c. getting a parking space   _____

2. Taking public transportation to work is usually _____.
    a. cheaper than driving
    b. less stressful than walking
    c. slower than cycling   _____

3. The cheapest way of getting to work is by _____.
    a. taking public transportation
    b. biking
    c. walking   _____

E INTERPRET. Complete the sentences about the pie chart.

1. In 2018, the second most popular way of commuting to work is by _____.
    a. public transportation   **b.** driving   **c.** biking or walking

2. _____ percent of commuters carpooled to work in 2018.
    a. 9.2   **b.** 2.7   **c.** 5.1

F INTERPRET VOCABULARY. Complete the sentences about the article.

1. The word *timetable* in line 8 means _____.
    a. a schedule   **b.** a ticket

2. The word *maintenance* in line 10 means _____.
    a. rental   **b.** repairs

3. The word *overcrowded* in line 17 means _____.
    a. full of people   **b.** dirty

G SUMMARIZE. What are the most important ideas in the article? Write three sentences.

_____

_____

_____

Lessons 5: Writing

A Read the Writing Skill. Read the text. Match the acronyms to the correct job duties.

<u>Senior Managers</u>
Most organizations have several senior managers. The most important one is the CEO (Chief Executive Officer). This is the person who leads the company and creates long-term plans for it. A CFO (Chief Financial Officer) manages a company's costs and makes sure it has enough money to operate. A CIO (Chief Information Officer) is the person who manages an organization's computers and information technology (IT). Finally, a CSO (Chief Security Officer) is responsible for physical security in a company.

> **Writing Skill: Define new words and acronyms**
> Give definitions when you introduce new words or acronyms. Introduce the definitions with a defining verb, such as *means* or *refers to*, or with parentheses ( ).

1. CEO ___   **a.** ensures that a company is making a profit

2. CFO ___   **b.** manages the security of company employees and equipment

3. CIO ___   **c.** makes plans for the future direction of a company

4. CSO ___   **d.** is responsible for setting up a company's computer network

B What is the correct definition of the acronym in this paragraph? Circle the letter.

Many companies have a CMO. This refers to the person who is responsible for getting new customers for the company, communicating with them, and thinking about how to meet their needs.
   a. Chief Media Officer
   b. Chief Marketing Officer
   c. Chief Management Officer

C Read the text. Correct three more errors.

If someone has a serious accident or is very sick, they are sometimes sent to an ICU (intensive care unit) in a hospital. In an ICE, doctors and nurses can watch the sick or injured person very closely. They can give the person different types of treatments. Some treatments might not work, but other one might. If the person gets worse, they may also be sent to an ER. This refer to the operating room where doctors perform certain medical procedures.

Lesson 6 & 7: Grammar

A Read the conversation. Then read the statements. Write *T* (True) or *F* (False).

Marcos: Fatima, do you mind covering for me next Tuesday? I need to go to the airport to pick up my son.

Fatima: Sure, no problem. Do you need me to cover any other days?

Marcos: Not right now, but I'll let you know. I'll cover for you, too, whenever you need.

Fatima: Great. How about covering for me next Friday? I have a doctor's appointment.

Marcos: Sure, no problem!

1. Marcos wants Fatima to cover for him next Friday. ____

2. Marcos needs Fatima to cover for him for two days. ____

3. Fatima asks Marcos to cover for her next Friday. ____

4. Fatima has a dentist's appointment next Friday. ____

B Write sentences. Put the words and phrases in the correct order.

1. (to close / needs / you / Sandra / the store)

_____

2. (you / early / me / do / to come / want / ?)

_____

3. (she / before 5:00 / me / does / expect / to finish / ?)

_____

4. (would like / his employee / to apologize / the manager / to a customer)

_____

5. (to clean / our work area / expects / us / the manager)

_____

C Read the email. Then complete the sentences.

1. Brian's boss expects _____
   _____.

2. Brian's boss requires _____
   _____.

3. Brian's boss wants _____
   _____.

4. Brian wants _____
   _____.

From:Brian811@myemail.com
To:JohnIngram@earthlinks.net

Hey John,

I started my new job last week. So far, I like working at Golden Sports. My boss is nice, but he is strict and expects us to follow the rules at all times. For example, he requires all employees to be at work five minutes before their shifts start. He also wants us to be friendly to customers and provide excellent customer service. There's a chance I might get promoted in a year or less. I want my boss to know that I'm an excellent worker, so I'm working hard.

Take care,
Brian

D Write sentences about the workplace notice. Use verb + object + infinitive.

Management kindly asks all employees to observe the following rules:

- After using the bathroom, all employees must wash their hands before returning to work.
- Keep your work area clean at all times.
- Tell your supervisor when an accident happens.
- Wear eye protection when operating any equipment.

● ● ●

1. *Management expects employees to wash their hands after using the bathroom.* _____

2. _____

3. _____

4. _____

E WRITE ABOUT IT. What does your supervisor or manager usually expect you to do? Write three sentences.

_____

_____

_____

Lesson 8: Workplace, Life, and Community Skills

A Read the safety notice. What should you do if someone has a back injury?

TO ENSURE YOUR SAFETY AND THAT OF YOUR CO-WORKERS, PLEASE FOLLOW THESE GUIDELINES:

- Report all injuries immediately to your supervisor.
- Do not try to treat your own injuries or someone else's injuries.
- In case of head, back, or leg injury, do not move the employee. Wait for medical attention from authorized personnel.
- Never distract the attention of another employee when the employee is working with machines. If you need the attention of another employee, wait until you can do so safely.
- Place materials, bins, boxes, equipment, etc. carefully so they don't block aisles, exits, firefighting equipment, etc.
  FIRE DOORS AND AISLES MUST BE KEPT CLEAR.
- Do not operate machines or equipment until you have been trained on how to use them.
- Do not operate machines or equipment unless you are authorized to do so by your supervisor.
- Report any UNSAFE condition to your supervisor.
- Lift properly—bend your knees, and keep your back straight. For heavier loads, ask for assistance.

When someone has a back injury, _____

_____

B Read the statements about the safety notice. Write *T* (True) or *F* (False).

1. It is OK to block an exit for 20 minutes. ____

2. It is OK to talk to employees when they are using a machine. ____

3. Keep your back bent when you lift heavy objects. ____

4. Any accidents or injuries must be reported immediately. ____

5. If an employee has a head injury, move him or her to a safe place, and then call 911. ____

C Match the danger to an accident it might cause.

1. A cup of coffee has spilled on the floor.   ____   **a.** You could trip over them.

2. A table saw has been left on after its use.   ____   **b.** It could fall on you.

3. A piece of equipment has been left on a high shelf.   ____   **c.** You might slip and fall.

4. There are loose cables on the floor.   ____   **d.** You might cut yourself.

D Look at the safety signs. Write each warning below the sign it corresponds to.

Wear safety boots	Wear goggles	Watch for forklifts
Caution: Trip hazard	Wear ear protection	Hot surface: Do not touch

1. _____.

2. _____.

3. _____.

4. _____.

5. _____.

6. _____.

E WRITE ABOUT IT. What are the most common safety hazards at your workplace? What safety signs are there to warn you about the hazards? List three of them.

_____

_____

_____

Lesson 9 & 10: Grammar

Ⓐ Read a manager's instructions to his employees. Change the direct speech to reported speech.

1. Manager: Put the boxes in the storage closet.

    Stefani: OK. No problem.

    The manager told Stefani to put the boxes in the storage closet.

2. Manager: Sweep up the aisle.

    Fred: Right away.

    _____

3. Manager: Don't open the store before 7:00.

    Thomas: Sure thing.

    _____

4. Manager: Call the supplier and order more materials.

    Sandra: OK.

    _____

Ⓑ The manager emailed a list of tasks to the employees. Read the list. Report the information. Use *tell* or *ask*.

1. *The manager tells the employees to put paper in the printers.*

2. _____

    _____

3. _____

    _____

4. _____

    _____

5. _____

    _____

From: Dereka@optline.com
To: group@optline.com

Important Tasks
- Put paper in the printers.
- Unplug the copier at the end of the day.
- Keep the warehouse clean and organized.
- Put the phones on "night mode" at the end of the day.
- Enter the security code and exit within 30 seconds when you leave.

Lesson 11: Soft Skills at Work

A UNDERSTAND. Complete the sentence. Circle the correct answer.

A person who listens actively _____.
- **a.** should never ask questions to clarify
- **b.** makes sure to understand what people say
- **c.** guesses what other people might want

B IDENTIFY. Read the conversations at work. In which conversations are the people listening actively? Check (✓) the conversations.

☐ **1. Dina:** Can you bring me those two boxes, please?

    Omar: Which ones do you want? These?

    Dina: No, the two small ones.

    Omar: Sure, no problem.

☐ **2. Lukas:** Good morning. How can I help you today?

    Customer: Hi. You delivered a new TV to my house today, but there's a crack in the screen!

    Lukas: I'm sorry, sir! There was a bad connection. Can you repeat that?

    Customer: I said that the TV you delivered today was damaged.

    Lukas: Oh! My apologies. Let's see what we can do for you.

☐ **3. Ardita:** Hi, Ana. Can you do me a favor? I need to pick up my brother from the airport next Tuesday. Can you cover for me that day?

    Ana: Did you say Tuesday or Thursday?

    Ardita: Tuesday.

    Ana: Oh, I'm sorry. I'm going on vacation tomorrow and won't be back until next Wednesday.

C ANALYZE. Read the conversations in Exercise B again. What are the different ways the people listen actively?

☐ **a.** figure out tasks or instructions later

☐ **b.** ask someone to repeat what they said

☐ **c.** guess what others want them to do

☐ **d.** ask questions if they're unsure about something

☐ **e.** repeat what someone has said to make sure they fully understand

Unit 10: Going to the Doctor

Lesson 1: Vocabulary

A Label the pictures.

admissions	laboratory	physical therapy
pediatrics	surgery	intensive care unit (ICU)

1. _____

2. _____

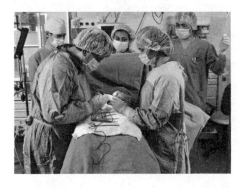

3. _____

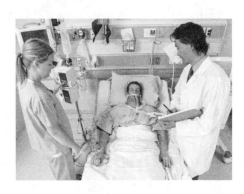

4. _____

5. _____

6. _____

B Complete the sentences. Use the words in Exercise A. Not all words will be used.

1. _____ is where patients check in.

2. _____ is where patients exercise to get better.

3. _____ is where doctors operate on patients.

4. _____ is where children receive medical care.

5. _____ is where patients' blood tests are sent.

C Complete the sentences. Use the words in the box.

laboratory	nurse's station	emergency room (ER)
maternity ward	radiology/imaging	intensive care unit (ICU)

1. Mr. Johnson is getting X-rays of his chest. He's in _____.

2. Sandra is in critical condition. She's recovering from surgery. She's staying in the

_____.

3. Mrs. Dang is having trouble breathing. She should go to the _____.

4. The nurse will be back in a moment. He's just getting your chart from the

_____.

5. Mr. Calvo's blood test results came back from the _____.

6. Olga is pregnant and is about to have a baby. She will be admitted to the

_____.

D WRITE ABOUT IT. If you worked in a hospital, what department or place would you like to work in? Why?

I would like to work in pediatrics. I like to take care of children.

_____

_____

_____

Lessons 2 & 3: Grammar

A Complete the sentences. Use the words in the box.

| confused | confusing | frustrated | frustrating | tired | tiring |

1. It's really _____ to get an incorrect medical bill. But don't get upset. You can always call the billing office and discuss it with them.

2. Are you too _____ to wait in line? Do you want to sit down and rest?

3. The patient was _____ because he didn't understand the doctor. The doctor used a lot of words the patient didn't know.

4. It can be _____ to get a blood test, especially if you haven't eaten anything in the past 12 hours.

5. Don't get _____ if you have to wait in line. This clinic is very busy.

6. Sometimes medicine labels are _____. Ask your pharmacist if you have questions.

B Cross out the incorrect words.

1. I'm **confused / confusing** about my medical bill. I can't understand it.

2. It's very **embarrassed / embarrassing** for some people to talk about medical problems.

3. I went to my appointment early, but it was **frustrated / frustrating** because I forgot my insurance card.

4. My pharmacist always explains how to take my prescription medicine. I'm always **interested / interesting** in talking with her.

5. It can be really **frightened / frightening** when you go to the ER.

6. I'm **tired / tiring** of waiting. I need to see the doctor soon.

C Use the -ed or -ing form of the word in parentheses.

1. Do large hospitals make you feel _____?
   (scare)

2. It can be _____ to see people in the ICU.
   (frighten)

3. Is she _____ with her doctor?
   (satisfy)

4. Did he get _____ when his doctor told him the good news?
   (excite)

5. My brother is _____ that his insurance won't cover the medications.
   (worry)

6. My sister thinks that hospitals are _____, and she would like
   (interest)
   to become a nurse.

D Answer the questions. Use the -ed or -ing form of the word in parentheses. Use the verbs be or feel.

1. How do some children feel when they visit the doctor?

   (scare) _They feel scared._____

2. Are instructions on medicine bottles difficult to understand?

   (confuse) _____

3. How do some patients feel with a doctor of the opposite sex?

   (embarrass) _____

4. The doctor told the patient that he would be fine. How does the patient feel?

   (relieve) _____

5. What is it like when patients have to wait a long time to see the doctor?

   (frustrate) _____

6. How do patients feel while waiting for test results?

   (stress) _____

Lesson 4: Workplace, Life, and Community Skills

A Read the medical history form. Answer the questions. Circle the correct answer.

MEDICAL HISTORY FORM   Date: _3/27/19_

Patient Name _Silva, Martim_   Date of Birth _6/18/72_

Reason for visit today: _Coughing, difficult to breathe_

How long have you had these symptoms? _Three days_

Have you been under a doctor's care in the last two years? ☑ Yes ☐ No

If yes, for what? _heart problems and high blood pressure_

Have you ever been hospitalized, had a major operation, or had a serious illness? ☑ Yes ☐ No
If yes, for what? _Asthma_

Please list any medications you are currently taking: _aspirin, diuretic_

_____

Are you allergic to any medications? ☐ Yes ☑ No

If yes, please list: _____

Do you now or have you ever had:

☐ Heart problems   ☐ Emphysema
☐ High blood pressure   ☐ Tuberculosis
☐ Diabetes   ☐ Hepatitis
☐ Cancer   ☐ Pneumonia
☐ Stroke   ☑ Asthma
☐ HIV/AIDS

In the past month, have you had any of the following symptoms?

☑ Weight gain or loss   ☐ Dizziness
☑ Chest pain   ☐ Nausea
☑ Shortness of breath   ☐ Stomach pain
☐ Fainting   ☐ Vomiting
☐ Headaches

---

1. What is the patient's first name?
    a. Silva   **b.** Martim

2. In what month does the patient visit the doctor?
    a. March   **b.** June

3. How long has the patient had symptoms?
    a. Less than a week   **b.** More than a week

4. What illness does the patient have a history of?
    a. Asthma   **b.** Diabetes

5. How many symptoms has the patient had in the past month?
    a. Two   **b.** Three

B WRITE ABOUT IT. Go online and find information about allergies to medication. What are three common drug allergies? What are some common symptoms for these allergies.

Drug	Symptom of allergy
Aspirin	Rash

C APPLY. Imagine you're a doctor. You took notes during Ms. Kim's appointment. Use these notes to fill out these sections of her medical history.

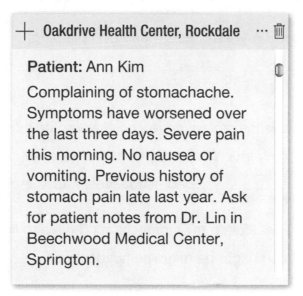

— Oakdrive Health Center, Rockdale ··· 🗑

Patient: Ann Kim

Complaining of stomachache. Symptoms have worsened over the last three days. Severe pain this morning. No nausea or vomiting. Previous history of stomach pain late last year. Ask for patient notes from Dr. Lin in Beechwood Medical Center, Springton.

Reason for patient's visit:

_____

How long has the patient had these symptoms?

_____

Has the patient been under a doctor's care in the last two years? ❑ Yes ❑ No.
If yes, for what?

_____

Lesson 5 & 6: Grammar

A Write sentences. Put the words in the correct order.

1. (bad headaches / has / my uncle / been / for three days / having)

   _____

2. (been / for two weeks / my aunt / coughing / has)

   _____

3. (not / sleeping / my husband / well / has / been)

   _____

4. (well / eating / not / been / have / I)

   _____

5. (about back pains / been / my daughter / has / complaining)

   _____

B Complete the conversation. Use the present perfect continuous and the verbs in parentheses.

Dr. Patel: Good morning, Mr. Cruz. What brings you here today?

Mr. Cruz: Well, _____ bad headaches. I have terrible pain in one temple,
　　　　　　　　　　　　1. (I / have)

　　　　　　　then the other. I get sick to my stomach, and I have to lie down in a dark room.

Dr. Patel: It sounds like these might be migraine headaches. _____ any
　　　　　　　　　　　　　　　　　　　　　　　　　　　　　　2. (you / take)

　　　　　　　medication?

Mr. Cruz: Yes, _____ pain relievers. That's all.
　　　　　　　　　　　3. (I / take)

Dr. Patel: Hmm. Your chart says you smoke. _____? Smoking makes
　　　　　　　　　　　　　　　　　　　　　　　4. (you / smoke)

　　　　　　　migraines worse.

Mr. Cruz: No, not really. _____ much. I'm trying to quit smoking.
　　　　　　　　　　　　　　5. (I / not / smoke)

Dr. Patel: OK. I'm going to prescribe some pain medication for your headaches. This is like
　　　　　　　over-the-counter pain relievers but a little stronger. Make an appointment to see me
　　　　　　　in one week.

Lesson 7: Reading

A **DEVELOP YOUR ACADEMIC SKILLS. Read the Academic Skill. Look at the table. Circle the correct answer. Complete the sentence.**

The topic of the text will be _____.
    a. ways to treat your child without medication
    b. what to do if your child has a rash
    c. childhood illnesses and how to treat them

> **Academic Skill:**
> **Interpret graphics**
>
> Looking at graphics, such as pictures and diagrams, helps you understand what an article is about. They show information in a visual format that is easy to see and understand.

B ▶ Listen and read.

CHILDHOOD ILLNESSES

Illness is a normal part of childhood. In fact, children get sick more often than adults. This is because their **immune systems** are still developing. They may still not be strong
5 enough to fight off all infections.

Here are four of the most common childhood illnesses and how to treat them.

Checklist: how to treat common childhood illnesses

Illness / Treatment	Common cold	Gastroenteritis	Chickenpox	Hand, foot, and mouth
Rest	✓	✓	✓	✓
Pain reliever			✓	✓
Extra liquids	✓	✓	✓	✓
Lotion			✓	

COMMON COLD

It is not unusual for a child to have up to five colds a year. Sore throat, headache, loss of appetite, mild fever,
10 and stuffed or runny nose are all signs that your child has a cold. Your child will also feel tired. Most colds clear up with rest, plenty of liquids, and time.

GASTROENTERITIS

This is more commonly known as "stomach flu" and is caused by a virus. Symptoms include stomach pain, nausea, and vomiting. The best treatment is rest. Make sure your child drinks more fluids than usual to replace
15 liquids lost through vomiting. Water is best. **Rehydration** drinks also contain sugar and salt that your child needs. If your child won't drink water, try diluted fruit juice or even popsicles!

CHICKENPOX

Chickenpox causes itchy rash and red spots. It is extremely **contagious**, even before symptoms appear. It can take more than two days to develop. Early symptoms include a fever and feeling ill. Then, spots appear on the
20 body. The spots develop into blisters filled with fluid, which can be very itchy. Try to stop your child from scratching the spots. This spreads infection and can cause scarring. **Lotion** can help to soothe the skin. Give a pain reliever if your child has a high fever.

HAND, FOOT, AND MOUTH

This is sometimes called "daycare disease" because it spreads quickly in settings where there are lots of
25 children. Children that have this disease often have a low fever, headache, and sore throat to start. A rash on the hands and feet may appear after a few days. Treat with rest, liquids, and pain relievers.

Parents often feel worried when a child is sick. However, not every illness requires a visit to the emergency room. Your child will usually get better with a little rest, a lot of liquids, and some pain relievers.

C **IDENTIFY. What is the main idea of the fourth paragraph?**

    a. Sick children should drink plenty of water but avoid other liquids.
    b. It is important to make sure your child drinks a lot of fluid when sick.
    c. Some foods count as liquid for your child.

D CITE EVIDENCE. Complete the sentences. Where is the information? Write the line number.

Lines

1. A child with a low fever and runny nose has symptoms of _____.
   a. a common cold   **b.** chickenpox   **c.** gastroenteritis   _____

2. The spots of chickenpox become itchy _____.
   a. when they first appear on the body
   b. when they become filled with fluid
   c. when they are rubbed with lotion   _____

3. Hand, foot, and mouth disease _____.
   a. begins with a rash
   b. affects only children who go to daycare
   c. spreads quickly in crowded places   _____

E INTERPRET. Complete the sentences about the table.

1. The most commonly recommended treatment for childhood illnesses is _____.
   a. to go to the emergency room   **b.** to take some pain relievers
   c. to rest and drink lots of fluid

2. Pain relievers are _____.
   a. not needed for every illness   **b.** good to use whenever your child is sick
   c. not safe to use with lotion

3. _____ is the only illness to need all four treatment types.
   a. The common cold   **b.** Chickenpox   **c.** Hand, foot, and mouth

F INTERPRET VOCABULARY. Complete the sentences.

1. The phrase *immune system* in line 3 means _____.
   a. protection given by vaccinations   **b.** how the body fights off illnesses

2. The word *rehydration* in line 15 means a drink that _____.
   a. replaces lost water   **b.** prevents further vomiting

3. The word *contagious* in line 18 means a disease that _____.
   a. can be passed from person to person   **b.** serious for your health

4. The word *lotion* in line 21 means _____.
   a. a type of cream you rub onto your skin   **b.** a type of medication

G SUMMARIZE. What are the most important ideas in the article? Write three sentences.

_____

_____

_____

Lesson 8: Writing

A Read the Writing Skill. Read the paragraph. Circle the best concluding sentence.

Healthy eating is not just about what you eat. It is also important to only eat the amount of food that your body actually needs. There are many simple ways to reduce the amount you eat. First, stop eating when you feel full and satisfied. Second, have a full plate of food but make sure you use a smaller plate! Third, focus on eating. Do not eat because you are bored, and do not eat in front of the TV.

> **Writing Skill: Write a concluding sentence**
>
> End your paragraph with a concluding sentence that summarizes the paragraph or gives an opinion on the topic. Use a concluding word or phrase such as *in conclusion*, *to conclude*, *therefore*, or *to sum up*.

a. In conclusion, you should eat regular meals and think about food all the time.
b. To sum up, small changes can make a big difference to your eating habits.
c. To conclude, healthy eating means having all meals at the table.

B Read the paragraphs. Check (✓) the paragraphs that have a concluding sentence.

❑ **1.** Marta goes to the gym every morning. She runs for 25 minutes. Then, she lifts weights for 20 minutes. After that, she takes a shower and gets dressed for work.

❑ **2.** Don takes his children to the park after school. They run around until it is time for dinner. They are always tired after the exercise. I think they are lucky to have so much time to play.

❑ **3.** Justin watches what he eats. He likes vegetables and eats them every day. He also likes ice cream, but he does not eat it often. Justin lives in Tampa, Florida.

C Read the text. Correct five more mistakes.

I think sleep is a̶ ^an̲ important part of a healthy lifestyle. It allows your body to rest and recover. It also gives you lots for energy. I have been try to form good sleeping habits for years. First, I turn off all screens one hour before bed. Then, I listen to music to relax. Finally, I have the cup of warm milk. Most nights I sleep for seven hours. It's very frustrated when I don't sleep well. I wake up tiring. In conclusion, I think more people should form good sleep habits.

Lesson 9 & 10: Grammar

A Complete the paragraph. Add the correct gerund form of the verbs.

Many people complain about _____ work or school when they are sick,
                                    1. (miss)

but it's important to remember that your health is more important. Sometimes people are

worried about _____ medical bills. If you are concerned about _____
                    2. (pay)   **3. (lose)**

pay or _____ behind on your work, just try to relax and get better.
            4. (fall)

B Read the text. Correct four more mistakes.

If people are serious ~~of~~ *about* taking care of their health, they should pay attention to their cholesterol levels. Many people are worried to getting high cholesterol. What is it, and why are people concerned for getting it? High blood cholesterol increases the risk of heart disease or stroke. Saturated fat in foods, like red meat and eggs, increases cholesterol levels. Smokers are also at risk for high cholesterol. People with high cholesterol usually don't have any symptoms. Control cholesterol is important. People who want to lower their cholesterol should think to quitting smoking. They also need to have a diet with less saturated fat, and they should exercise. It is also important to have your cholesterol checked regularly.

C Complete the sentences with your information. Use gerunds.

1. I'm worried about _____.

2. I don't believe in _____.

3. I complain about _____.

Lesson 11: Soft Skills at Work

A DEFINE. Complete the sentence. Circle the answer.

A person who prioritizes responsibilities _____.
- **a.** puts family before work
- **b.** puts customers first
- **c.** does tasks in order of importance

B IDENTIFY. Read the conversations at work. In which conversations do the people prioritize tasks? Check (✓) the conversations.

❑ **1. Manager:** OK, so we're pretty busy this morning. The moms in maternity ward B need medications. They're exhausted because their babies have been crying all morning. The babies in ward C need baths. Anything else?

    Nurse: A mom just arrived in ward A. She's worried about feeding her baby.

    Manager: Let's check on her right away. She sounds like she needs help. Then, we'll give out medications. The baths can wait.

❑ **2. Sam:** You look confused. Are you okay?

    Ming: Ms. Vega needed some files for an important meeting. She asked me this morning at the laboratory but I forgot about them. I'm not used to taking care of so many things. I have been working on other tasks, and I didn't have them ready on time.

    Sam: Next time, write it all down. That way you'll see what order you need to do the work.

    Ming: You're right. A list is a good idea.

❑ **3. Jane:** I'm exhausted! We've been working all day and there's still a lot to do. I'm worried about getting everything finished.

    Mark: Well, we need to mop the floor, right? That will take a while. Emptying the trash and cleaning the tables will be quick jobs.

    Jane: OK, I'll start with those. Then we'll have time to do the floors properly.

    Mark: Yes, and we can plan tomorrow's menu while we wait for the floors to dry.

C ANALYZE. Read the conversations in Exercise B again. What are the different ways the people prioritize tasks?

❑ **a.** write a list   ❑ **d.** check what is urgent

❑ **b.** ask for more information   ❑ **e.** do quicker tasks first

❑ **c.** do the task with the greatest value

Lesson 1: Vocabulary

A Label the pictures.

ATM/debit card	bank teller	credit card
ATM withdrawal	check	bank statement

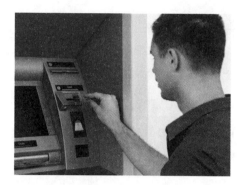

1. _____

2. _____

3. _____

4. _____

5. _____

6. _____

B Circle the items that match the sentences.

1. This list gives all the bank transactions you made for the month.
   a. balance   **b.** bank statement   **c.** check

2. You buy things and pay for them later with this plastic card.
   a. credit card   **b.** ATM/debit card   **c.** check

3. This is the amount of money in an account.
   a. bank statement   **b.** check   **c.** balance

4. You write on this to pay for something.
   a. check   **b.** ATM/debit card   **c.** bank statement

C Complete the sentences. Use the words in the box.

withdrawal	bank statement	credit card	balance	bank teller	check

1. Kate doesn't know how much money is in her checking account. She needs to check her

   _____ .

2. Thomas was not careful with his _____ balance. He didn't pay it off, and now

   he owes a lot of money!

3. The bank should hire another _____ . There are always long lines in the

   afternoon.

4. You can make a _____ with your ATM card at any time of the day or night.

5. You can sometimes purchase items with a _____ if you don't have any cash or

   cards with you.

6. A _____ helps you remember the checks you wrote.

D WRITE ABOUT IT. What banking services or products do you prefer to use? Why?

I always make deposits and withdrawals with a bank teller. I never use the ATM.

I'm afraid to make a mistake.

_____

_____

_____

Lessons 2 & 3: Grammar

A Put *if* and the sentences in the correct order. More than one answer is possible.

1. (if / you may have to pay a large fee / you don't pay your credit card bill on time)

_____

2. (you can save time and money on stamps / if / you pay your bills online)

_____

3. (you open an online savings account / you can get a high interest rate / if)

_____

4. (if / call the credit card company immediately / you lose your credit card)

_____

5. (you change your PIN often / if / you can keep your account safe)

_____

B Read the bank advertisement. Write sentences about the information.
Use the present real conditional.

Save-U-More Bank

☑ **Free checking**
when you open an account online

☑ **Free ATM/debit card**
when you open an account

☑ **Free checks for 12 months**
if you open an account this month

☑ **$50 cash bonus**
for new accounts after they are
open for six months

☑ 24/7 customer support for online customers

1. _You can get free checking if you open an account online._

2. _____

3. _____

4. _____

5. _____

Lesson 4: Reading

A ▶ Listen and read.

THE BENEFITS OF ONLINE BANKS

Online banks are banks that don't have a physical branch. Many people think they are not as safe as traditional banks. In fact, online banks are now very safe. They have other benefits, too.

5 **LOWER (OR NO) FEES**
Many traditional banks charge high fees for checking accounts. This is because setting up physical **branches** and paying employees are expensive. For online banks, these expenses are
10 much lower. They can then charge lower fees. Some online banks don't charge any monthly fees.

Traditional banks often charge transfer fees. Most online banks don't charge this fee, either.

With physical banks, you might have to pay a fee
15 if you **make a withdrawal** with your ATM card. A lot of online banks don't charge this fee. Sometimes, they do. However, they may **reimburse** you the fee if you keep a certain amount of money in your account.

HIGHER INTEREST RATES
In the U.S., the average savings interest rate is 0.06 percent. Most online banks offer a higher rate. Some offer
20 up to 1.5 percent if you meet certain requirements. For example, if you have $10,000 in savings, at a rate of 0.06 percent a year, you would only earn $6 after one year. With a rate of 1.5 percent, you would earn $150!

MORE CONVENIENT
Online banks are very easy to use. You can pay your bills any time using a computer or a smartphone. You can also easily see all your transactions.

25 In addition, online accounts save your payment information. This means you don't have to enter the same information every time you want to pay someone.

Online banks are a safe – and cheaper – banking option. They are also always open. If you need to save time and money, an online bank may be a good option for you.

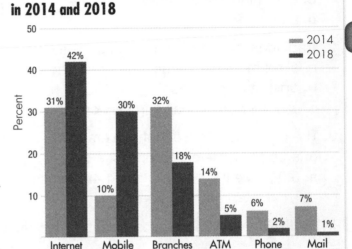

How Americans accessed their bank accounts in 2014 and 2018

Legend: 2014, 2018

Internet 31% / 42%
Mobile App 10% / 30%
Branches 32% / 18%
ATM 14% / 5%
Phone 6% / 2%
Mail 7% / 1%

B DEVELOP YOUR ACADEMIC SKILLS. Read the Academic Skill. Answer the question.

What do you think is the author's purpose?
   a. To give information about how to open an online bank account
   b. To make an argument about the benefits of online banks
   c. To inform about the different types of online bank accounts

> **Academic Skill: Identify author's purpose**
> Writers have a purpose (or reason) for writing. Their purpose can be to give information, make an argument, or entertain. Sometimes a writer has more than one purpose.

C IDENTIFY. What is the main idea of the article?

a. Online banks are cheaper and more convenient than traditional banks.
b. Online banks never charge fees for transactions.
c. Traditional banks offer the best interest rates for savings accounts.

D CITE EVIDENCE. Complete the sentences. Where is the information? Write the line number.

Lines

1. Many online banks _____.
   a. have physical branches
   b. offer high interest rates
   c. aren't very safe
   _____

2. Traditional banks often charge a fee if you _____.
   a. send money to an account at a different bank
   b. open a new account
   c. use their online banking services
   _____

3. The difference between the average savings interest rate and the rate offered by some online banks is _____.
   a. 0.9 percent   **b.** 1.44 percent   **c.** 1.5 percent   _____

E INTERPRET. Answers the questions about the chart.

1. In 2018, what was the second most popular method of accessing bank accounts?
   a. Internet   **b.** Mobile app   **c.** Branches

2. Which banking method was the least popular among Americans in 2014?
   a. ATM   **b.** Phone   **c.** Mail

3. Which of the following statement is true?
   a. The popularity of using mobile apps to access bank accounts increased by 15%.
   b. The popularity of visiting bank branches decreased the most compared to the other methods.
   c. Accessing bank accounts by mail was one of the most popular methods in 2014.

F INTERPRET VOCABULARY. Complete the sentences.

1. The word *branch* in line 8 means _____.
   a. a location that belongs to a company   **b.** a person who works in a bank

2. The phrase *make a withdrawal* in line 14 mean _____.
   a. take out money   **b.** put in money

3. The word *reimburse* in line 15 means _____.
   a. to pay money back   **b.** to charge a fee

G SUMMARIZE. What are the most important ideas in the article? Write three sentences.

_____

_____

_____

Lessons 5: Writing

A DEVELOP YOUR ACADEMIC SKILLS. Read the Writing Skill. Which paragraphs include specific examples?

a. There are many ways you can save money on food expenses. For example, buy less takeout food and cook at home more often.

b. To reduce your water bill, try to use less water. It's also better for the environment if you use less water.

c. Driving to work can be expensive. However, if you use cheaper options, such as cycling or walking, you can save a lot of money.

d. Use coupons when you shop. They can save you a lot of money.

B Match each topic sentence with the example it corresponds to.

1. There are lots of ways to save on banking fees. ___

2. Public transportation can be a big expense, but there are ways to save. ___

3. To meet your financial goals, try to change your spending habits. ___

a. Some tickets, such as weekly or monthly tickets, are cheaper than buying a round-trip ticket every day.

b. For example, make your own lunch every day, or buy clothes in thrift stores.

c. For instance, if you switch to an online bank, you can avoid transfer fees.

C Read the text. Correct four more errors.

In addition to utility bills, cell phone bills can sometimes be expensive. However, there ~~is~~ *are* ways to reduce these bills. Example, you could change your cell phone carrier. If you compare different plans online, you can never find a good deal. Check out what is included in each plan, such talk, text, and data per month. Some cell phone services also offer special discounts. For examples, if you call a certain country very often, some services offer a lower rate to call that country.

Lessons 6 & 7: Grammar

A Cross out the incorrect verbs.

1. If you go to a thrift store, you ~~find~~ / **might find** clothes at low prices.

2. Your clothes will last longer if you **follow** / **will follow** the cleaning instructions on the tag.

3. If you shop for clothes during holiday sales, the stores **offer** / **might offer** big savings.

4. You might save money if you **might shop** / **shop** online and look for coupons.

5. If you **get** / **will get** summer clothes in the fall, you might find a lot of sales.

B Make future real conditionals with the verbs in parentheses. More than one answer is sometimes possible.

1. If you _____ the newspaper, you _____ good deals on rentals.
   (check)   (find)

2. If you _____ insurance for your home, you _____ your things.
   (get)   (be able to protect)

3. Their electric bill _____ if they _____ the heat low.
   (go down)   (keep)

4. You _____ if you _____ to do small repairs yourself.
   (save money)   (learn)

5. If you _____ leaks around your windows, you _____ on
   (fix)   (save money)

   heating and cooling.

6. If you _____ a long-term lease, you _____ on your rent.
   (sign)   (save)

C WRITE ABOUT IT. Look at the categories in the box. What are ways you can save money on these things? Write two ways to save money for each category. Use future real conditionals.

| appliances | furniture | entertainment |

If you buy appliances on sale, you will save money.

_____

_____

_____

_____

_____

_____

Lesson 8: Workplace, Life, and Community Skills

A Look at Sarah's gas bill. Circle the amount due this month.

Your Account Number
987 654 320 3
Sarah Sandoval
2947 W. Toller Rd.
Fullerton, CA 91789

24-Hour Service and info
(800) 555-2000

Seneca Gas
PO Box A
Monterey Park, CA 94175
www.senecagas.com

Billing Period	Meter number	Next meter reading date on or around Nov. 5, 2019
From 9/08/19 to 10/08/19	06076856	

Previous Charges	Account Balance
Total Amount Due at Last Billing	$124.77
Payment—9/15/19	$124.77
Previous Balance	$0.00

Current Charges	Amount
Customer Charge 30 Days	$5.17
Electricity Charges	$134.42
Taxes and Fees	$7.79
Total Electric Charges including taxes and fees	$147.38
Total Amount Due	**$147.38**

Current Amount Past Due
If not paid by 10/31/19, a late charge of $10.00 may apply.

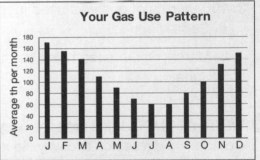

Your Gas Use Pattern

Energy Tip: We measure gas by the therm (th). When you read your utility bill, th shows how much gas you used.

Special DiscountYou may be eligible for California Alternate Rates for Energy (CARE) program. For more information and to request an application, please call 1(800) 555-5050.*

B Look at the bill again. Read the statements below. Write *T* (true) or *F* (false).

1. The billing period is September 8, 2018 to October 8, 2019. _____

2. The next meter reading date will be on or around 11/5/19. _____

3. Last month's bill was $147.38. _____

4. This month Sarah must pay $7.79 in taxes and fees. _____

5. The total amount due is $134.42. _____

6. If Sarah pays before October 30, 2019, she must pay a late charge. _____

C Look at the graph on the bill. Complete the sentences. Circle the correct answers.

1. In the graph, *th* represents _____.
   a. the units of gas used   **b.** the amount of money spent on gas

2. The least amount of gas was used in _____.
   a. June and July   **b.** July and August

3. 100 therms of gas was used in _____.
   a. September   **b.** October

4. In March, Sarah used twice as much gas as she did in _____.
   a. June   **b.** July

D WRITE ABOUT IT. What are some ways you can save money on your utility bills? Go online and research two ways to reduce each bill.

Gas	*When heating your house, make sure all the windows and doors are closed.*
Electricity	
Water	

Lesson 9 & 10: Grammar

A Write sentences. Put the words in the correct order.

1. (renting / don't mind / a room / I)

   _____

2. (to live / we / near the city / prefer)

   _____

3. (loves / she / close to work / living)

   _____

4. (us / the manager / to see / promised)

   _____

5. (the living room / they / painting / finished)

   _____

6. (need / we / to pay / all utilities)

   _____

B Cross out the incorrect words.

1. I can't afford **to live / living** in that house.

2. I finished **to talk / talking** to the apartment manager.

3. Do you feel like **to look / looking** at some more apartments?

4. We need **to wait / waiting** for the manager's phone call.

5. I hope **to move / moving** in to my new apartment next month.

6. She doesn't mind **to live / living** downtown.

C Complete the email. Use gerunds or infinitives.

From: maha@earthinks.net
To: rico@myemail.com

Dear Rico,

I just moved in to my new place! I found a great little apartment near my son's school. I don't mind _____ here because it's close to
1. (live)
many stores I like. I can walk to the supermarket. Do you know how I picked my apartment? Well, you know that I planned _____ an
2. (have)
apartment with three bedrooms. The manager told me she only had one three-bedroom apartment left. She also said that I could get two months free if I made a deposit that day. So I made a deposit and moved in the next day! I didn't even feel like _____ at other
3. (look)
places. Well, I need to finish _____.
4. (unpack)

Write me back!
Maha

D WRITE ABOUT IT. What kind of housing do you want or need? Use the words in the box and your own ideas. Use gerunds and infinitives.

like/don't like	need/don't need	hope	can afford/can't afford
plan/don't plan	want/don't want	prefer	don't mind

I prefer to live near a park. I don't want to live on a busy street. I like walking to work.

_____

_____

_____

Lesson 11: Soft Skills at Work

A THINK CRITICALLY. Complete the sentence. Circle the correct answer.

A person who thinks critically at work _____.
- **a.** considers different people's points of view
- **b.** always follows their manager's instructions
- **c.** takes the initiative without asking others

B IDENTIFY. Read the situations at work. In which situations do the people think critically? Check (✓) the situations.

❑ **1.** Justin's manager wants to reduce costs in their department. She thinks the best way to do this is to have Justin start working part-time. She says that if the company cuts his hours, it will save a lot of money. Justin quickly agrees, and he says he wouldn't mind working part-time.

❑ **2.** Aki is speaking to an angry customer. He bought a defective TV and wants a refund. She's not sure what to do, and she tells the customer she'll call him back. After speaking with one of her co-workers, she calls the customer back. She says that she can send a technician to fix the TV.

❑ **3.** Ren is planning to rent a new apartment that's bigger, but he can't afford to pay the security deposit for it. He needs to get a raise. Before he talks to his manager, he speaks with his co-workers about the best way to ask for a raise.

❑ **4.** Ali needs to improve sales of his company's kitchen utensils, so he plans to find out more about what customers enjoy cooking. To do this, he asks his manager and co-workers to help him design an online customer survey.

C ANALYZE. Read the situations in Exercise B again. What are the different ways the people think critically?

❑ **a.** try to understand other people's opinions

❑ **b.** ask for co-workers' help before making a decision

❑ **c.** use different types of resources available to them

❑ **d.** make a quick decision before getting more information

Lesson 1: Vocabulary

A Match the pictures with the places.

 a.

 b.

 c.

 d.

 e.

 f.

 g.

 h.

1. Capitol Building   _a_   **2.** Jefferson Memorial   ___

3. Lincoln Memorial   ___   **4.** Pentagon   ___

5. Supreme Court   ___   **6.** U.S. Treasury   ___

7. Washington Monument   ___   **8.** White House   ___

B Circle the correct places that match their descriptions.

1. The Senate and the House of Representatives write laws here.
   a. White House   **b.** Capitol Building   **c.** Supreme Court

2. Judges explain the law here.
   a. White House   **b.** Capitol Building   **c.** Supreme Court

3. The president lives and works here.
   a. White House   **b.** Capitol Building   **c.** Supreme Court

4. This place honors the president who ended slavery.
   a. Lincoln Memorial   **b.** Jefferson Memorial   **c.** Washington Monument

5. This place honors the third president of the United States.
   a. Lincoln Memorial   **b.** Jefferson Memorial   **c.** Washington Monument

C Complete the sentences. Use the places in the box.

Capitol Building	Smithsonian Institution	White House
Pentagon	Washington Monument	

1. The _____ is a building with five sides that serves as the headquarters of the U.S. Department of Defense.

2. There are beautiful paintings at the _____.

3. You might meet a senator or a representative if you visit the _____.

4. If you want to see a view of Washington, D.C., visit the _____.

5. The president and the First Family live in the _____.

D WRITE ABOUT IT. Think of one place in Washington, D.C., you want to visit. Why do you want to visit this place? What will you do there?

I would like to visit the Capitol Building. I want to learn how Congress makes laws.

_____

_____

_____

Lessons 2 & 3: Grammar

Ⓐ Cross out the incorrect words.

1. My mother works in the White House, and my sister ~~do~~ / **does,** too.

2. We don't go traveling often, and my parents **doesn't** / **don't**, either.

3. Pablo didn't like the crowds at the festival, and Maria **doesn't** / **didn't**, either.

4. We enjoyed the museums in Washington, D.C., and our son **did** / **does**, too.

5. They don't know the city well, and he **doesn't** / **don't**, either.

6. I didn't know how to get to the Lincoln Memorial, and my husband **doesn't** / **didn't**, either.

7. Jon wants to know more about the history of the U.S. Treasury, and his children **do** / **does**, too.

Ⓑ Combine the sentences. Use *do, too / does, too / don't, either / doesn't, either.*

1. My grandmother lives in Dallas. My aunt and cousins live in Dallas.

   My grandmother lives in Dallas, and my aunt and cousins do, too.

2. We take the subway to school. Our neighbor takes the subway to school.

   _____

3. You don't want to miss the tour of the Oval Office. I don't want to miss the tour of the Oval Office.

   _____

4. They go to the park after class each day. Their friends go to the park after class each day.

   _____

5. His parents like visiting the Smithsonian Institution. He likes visiting the Smithsonian Institution.

   _____

6. I don't like to travel by bus. She doesn't like to travel by bus.

   _____

7. My father buys his museum tickets online. My daughter buys her museum tickets online.

   _____

Lesson 4: Workplace, Life, and Community Skills

A Look at the subway map. Answer the questions.

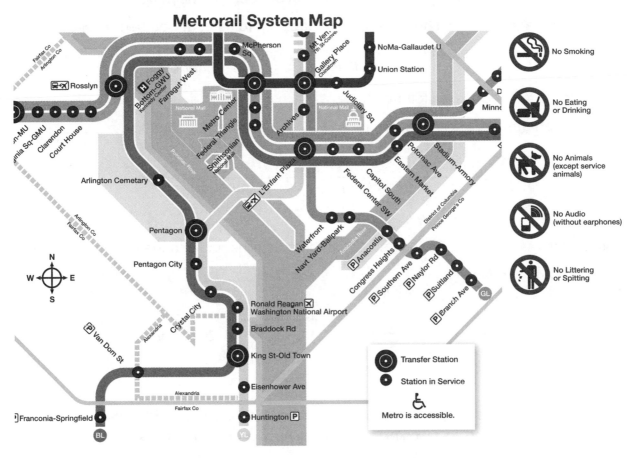

Metrorail System Map

1. You are on the blue line at King St-Old Town going to Ronald Reagan/Washington National Airport. Are you going north, south, east, or west?

   _____.

2. Which line goes to Arlington Cemetery?

   _____.

3. Can you eat on the subway?

   _____.

4. How many lines go to L'Enfant Plaza?

   _____.

5. You are on the orange line at Court House going to Potomac Ave. Are you going north, south, east, or west?

   _____.

6. Which lines go to Gallery Place?

   _____.

B Look at the subway map in Exercise A. Complete the sentences.

Passenger: I'm trying to get to Union Station. Can you help me?

Station manager: Let me show you on the map. You're here, at Southern Avenue. You need to take the _____ going _____ to Gallery Place.
　　　　　　　　　　　　　　　　　1. *(line)*　　　　　　　　2. *(direction)*

Passenger: Can I walk from there?

Station manager: Yes, it's a 20-minute walk. Or you can change to the _____
　　　　　　　　　　　　　　　　　　　　　　　　　　　　　　　　　　　　　3. *(line)*

going _____ for _____ stops. That will bring you
　　　　4. *(direction)*　　　　　5. *(number)*

right to the station.

Passenger: Great! So, I go south on the green line and change lines after two stops?

Station manager: No, it's _____ on the _____ and change at
　　　　　　　　　　　　6. *(direction)*　　　　　　　　7. *(line)*

_____. Then it's another _____ stops.
8. *(station name)*　　　　　　　　　　9. *(number)*

Passenger: Okay, got it! Thanks.

C WRITE ABOUT IT. Use an app for public transportation in your city to find the quickest route between your home and your workplace or school. Answer these questions.

1. How long does the journey take?

_____

2. Is this the way you usually travel to work or school? Why or why not?

_____

_____

3. Is there another way according to the app? Describe it in one or two sentences.

_____

_____

Lessons 5 & 6: Grammar

A Put the words and phrases in the correct order. More than one answer is possible.

1. (by the president / signed / are / new laws)

_____

2. (laws / are / by the Judiciary / enforced)

_____

3. (is / as the supreme law of the land / the U.S. Constitution / known)

_____

4. (are / every six years / elected / state senators)

_____

B Complete the sentences. Use the simple present passive and the verbs in parentheses.

1. San Francisco _____ by more people than any other city.
                          (visit)

2. The state of Washington _____ after President Washington.
                                  (name)

3. The Virginia towns of Williamsburg, Jamestown, and Yorktown _____
                                                                    (know)

as the Historic Triangle.

4. The Statue of Liberty _____ by millions of people every year.
                              (see)

C Rewrite the sentences. Use the simple present passive.

1. Congress creates laws in the Capitol Building.

   Laws are created by Congress in the Capitol Building. _____

2. Every four years, registered voters choose the president of the United States.

_____

3. The president chooses members for the cabinet.

_____

4. The president controls the U.S. military.

_____

► Listen and read.

A HISTORY IN BUILDINGS

Washington, D.C., was set up as a place for the government to do its work. The story of the U.S. and its leaders is marked by the city's buildings. Many people visit these buildings to learn more about U.S. history.

5 **THE WHITE HOUSE**
The White House is one of the world's most famous buildings. It was built so that the president could live and work in one place. George Washington chose the site in 1791. President John Adams moved in eight years later. Since then, every U.S. president has
10 lived in the White House. The building has changed over the years. The British burned it down in 1814. It had to be rebuilt. Later, new work spaces were added, too. These included the West **Wing** and the Oval Office. In 1901, President Theodore Roosevelt named the building the "White House."

Top 10 countries for overseas visitors to Washington, D.C. (2017)

Country	Number of visitors
1. China	324K
2. U.K.	194K
3. Germany	136K
4. South Korea	131K
5. France	94K
6. Australia	90K
7. India	80K
8. Spain	64K
9. Italy	63K
10. Japan	62K

15 **ARLINGTON NATIONAL CEMETERY**
The land at Arlington National Cemetery was once owned by a rich family. They had many slaves. Federal troops took over the land in the Civil War. In 1863, the government set up Freedman's Village there. It helped slaves to start new lives. The government bought the land in 1864. The city had no more space to bury soldiers. Some of the land became a national cemetery for members of the armed forces. President John Fitzgerald
20 Kennedy and his brother, Senator Robert Kennedy, are buried at Arlington. The cemetery is still used today.

ROOSEVELT MEMORIAL
Great presidents are remembered at the National **Mall**. Franklin D. Roosevelt led the U.S. through the Great **Depression** and World War II. He is the only president to have served more than two terms.

Roosevelt's monument has four parts. Each one stands for a term in office. There are lots of water features. They
25 all have meanings, too. One marks the crash of the economy in 1929. Another marks the New Deal programs to create jobs. The others mark World War II and Roosevelt's death in 1945.

The history of Washington, D.C, can be seen in the city's buildings. They often tell the story of the U.S. as a whole.

 DEVELOP YOUR ACADEMIC SKILLS. Read the Academic Skill. Read the fifth paragraph. Choose the sentence that summarizes this paragraph.

a. The design of the Roosevelt Memorial tells us about the life of a great U.S. president.

b. The Roosevelt Memorial is one of many monuments on the National Mall.

c. Franklin D. Roosevelt created many jobs in the U.S. after World War II.

Academic Skill: Summarize

When you summarize a text, you state or write the most important ideas or information in the text. Summarizing helps you check your understanding and remember what you read.

C IDENTIFY. What is the main idea of the article? Circle the correct answer.

The historical buildings of Washington, D.C. _____.
   a. are the most famous in the world
   b. reflect the history of the U.S.
   c. celebrate great presidents of the U.S.

D CITE EVIDENCE. Complete the sentences. Where is the information? Write the line number.

Lines

1. _____ was the first president to live in the White House.
   a. George Washington   b. John Adams   c. Theodore Roosevelt   _____

2. _____ gave the president's house its name.
   a. George Washington   b. John Adams   c. Theodore Roosevelt   _____

3. Franklin D. Roosevelt served as president for _____ terms.
   a. two   b. three   c. four   _____

E INTERPRET. Complete the sentences about the table.

1. Washington, D.C., received _____ overseas visitors in 2017.
   a. around 1.2 million   b. more than 1.5 million   c. more than 1.8 million

2. Most European visitors came from _____.
   a. Italy   b. Germany   c. the U.K.

3. Around _____ more visitors came to Washington, D.C., from Italy than from Japan.
   a. one thousand   b. two thousand   c. three thousand

F INTERPRET VOCABULARY. Complete the sentences.

1. The word *wing* in line 15 means a part of a building that is _____.
   a. joined to the side of the main building   b. used by office workers

2. The word *mall* in line 23 means _____.
   a. a park area designed for walking   b. a group of shops that are connected

3. The word *depression* in line 24 means a time when _____.
   a. many businesses are failing   b. people are unhappy with their lives

G SUMMARIZE. What are the most important ideas in the article? Write three sentences.

_____

_____

_____

Lesson 8 & 9: Grammar

(A) Put the words and phrases in the correct order.

1. (was / the location of / chosen / Washington, D.C. / by Alexander Hamilton)

   _____

2. (Pierre L'Enfant / by President Washington / selected / to design Washington, D.C. / was)

   _____

3. (was / by / freedom / Washington's army / American / won)

   _____

4. (by Thomas Jefferson / was / The Declaration of Independence / written)

   _____

(B) Complete the sentences. Use the simple present passive and the verbs in parentheses.

1. The White House ___was designed___ by architect James Hoban.
   (design)

2. The White House _____ between 1792 and 1800.
   (build)

3. The White House _____ by the British in 1814.
   (burn down)

4. Soldiers _____ in the East Room during the Civil War.
   (house)

5. Electricity _____ in the White House in 1891.
   (install)

6. The Oval Office and the Cabinet Room _____ in 1909.
   (add)

C Complete the paragraph. Use the past passive.

The Articles of Confederation _____*were used*_____ as the first constitution for the United States.
1. (use)

This was during the 1780s. The first rights _____ by the Articles. For example,
2. (establish)

freedom of movement _____ by the Articles. This means that people could travel
3. (grant)

freely from state to state. Also, under the Articles, the federal government _____
4. (give)

the power to declare war and make treaties. However, it _____ to collect taxes
5. (not / allow)

or make money! The Articles _____ as weak. The Articles _____
6. (see) **7. (replace)**

by the U.S. Constitution in 1789.

D Write past passive sentences.

1. John Adams / elect / as the second president of the U.S.

John Adams was elected as the second president of the U.S.

2. In the 1780s, money / create / by each state.

_____

3. In 1865, slavery / made / illegal in the U.S.

_____

4. The British / defeat / in the War of Independence.

_____

E WRITE ABOUT IT. What parts of U.S. history do you want to learn more about? The presidents?
The Constitution? Write three sentences.

I want to learn more about the U.S. Constitution. I think the U.S. Constitution is the best constitution
ever written.

_____

_____

_____

Lesson 10: Writing

A Read the paragraph. List the sensory words. Each category should have two words.

One of my favorite places in Washington, D.C. is the Sculpture Garden at the National Gallery of Art. I like the garden the best on bright winter days. I look at the beautiful works of art as I walk through it. At the ice rink, I listen to the loud happy shouts of people skating. I love the feeling of icy air on my face as I skate and the smell of salty popcorn and spiced cakes from the café. Afterwards, I drink sweet strong coffee with my friends. The warm cup feels good in my hands!

Sight: _bright,_ _____   **Taste:** _____

Smell: _____   **Touch:** _____

Sound: _loud,_ _____

B WRITE ABOUT IT. Complete the paragraph with the sensory words in the box.

bitter	cold	strong	warm

The iced tea at the café was not very good. There was not enough ice in it. I wanted something __cold__ to drink, but it was _____. It was also made with too much water and lemon. I like my tea to taste _____. Then, I had to add more sugar because it tasted so _____! I won't buy iced tea there again.

C Read the text. Correct four more mistakes.

                                        the
I have some tips for your visit to ~~a~~ museum next week! The sandwiches at the café is good value, and the soups are, to. The fries smell great. However, the portions aren't very large, and the salads are, either. People were complaining about the prices. The cakes are locate beside the cash register. They taste really fresh. Be sure to try some herbal tea. The mint is grown in the museum garden. Look for a table upstairs. Lots of groups are seated in the main dining area, and it was very noisy.

Lesson 11: Soft Skills at Work

A LOCATE INFORMATION. Complete the sentence. Circle the correct answer.

A person who is good at locating information _____.
   a. is able to find an answer right away
   b. is not comfortable asking for help
   c. is quick to think of ways to overcome a difficulty

B IDENTIFY. Read the conversations at work. In which conversations do the people locate information? Check (✓) the conversations.

❑ **1. Customer:**   Hi, do you know where I can find a turkey?

   Shop worker: Sure, the freezers are located in aisle D.

   Customer: Thanks. What about fresh cranberries?

   Shop worker: I think they're out of stock. Let me ask my supervisor.

❑ **2. Visitor:**   Excuse me! I'd like to see Benjamin Franklin's walking stick. Which room is it in?

   Museum guide: That's not on this floor anymore.

   Visitor: Do you know where it has been moved to?

   Museum guide: No, I'm new here. You could go back to the information desk. Someone there might know.

❑ **3. Woman:**   Hi, I'm visiting this weekend. Do I need to buy subway tickets for my children?

   Subway worker: Well, what ages are they?

   Woman: My son is four, and my daughter is nearly two.

   Subway worker: I'm going to have a look at my manual here. No, that's what I thought. You don't need tickets for them. Children aged five or under can ride for free.

C ANALYZE. Read the situations in Exercise B again. What are the different ways the people locate information.

❑ **a.** asks a co-worker   ❑ **d.** checks a manual

❑ **b.** talks to a customer again   ❑ **e.** asks a supervisor

❑ **c.** searches online   ❑ **f.** checks over notes

My Soft Skills Log

This is a list of my soft skills. They are skills I use every day. They are important for work, school, and home. In a job interview, I can talk about my soft skills. I can give these examples from my life.

Unit 1: I'm inclusive.

For example, _____

_____

_____

_____

Unit 2: I take responsibility for professional growth.

For example, _____

_____

_____

_____

Unit 3: I separate work life and family life.

For example, _____

_____

_____

_____

Unit 4: I'm positive.

For example, _____

_____

_____

_____

Unit 5: I find creative solutions.

For example, _____

_____

_____

_____

Unit 6: I respond to customer needs.

For example, _____

_____

_____

_____

Unit 7: I'm flexible.

For example, _____

_____

_____

_____

Unit 8: I take initiative.

For example, _____

_____

_____

_____

Unit 9: I listen actively.

For example, _____

_____

_____

_____

Unit 10: I prioritize.

For example, _____

_____

_____

_____

Unit 11: I think critically.

For example, _____

_____

_____

_____

Unit 12: I locate information.

For example, _____

_____

_____

_____

Writing Checklist

Check your writing for each unit. Does it have everything in the list?

Unit 1
- ❑ Does the paragraph have a topic sentence?
- ❑ Does the topic sentence give the main idea of the paragraph?
- ❑ Does the paragraph say who moved and where?
- ❑ Does the paragraph say why the writer moved?

Unit 2
- ❑ Does the paragraph have a topic sentence?
- ❑ Does the topic sentence explain the goal?
- ❑ Does the paragraph have supporting sentences?
- ❑ Do the steps begin with *first*, *next*, *then*, *last*, or *finally*?

Unit 3
- ❑ Does the paragraph have a topic sentence that gives an opinion?
- ❑ Does the paragraph include reasons that support this opinion?
- ❑ Does the paragraph include words such as *first*, *second*, and *finally*?

Unit 4
- ❑ Does the cover letter begin with an introduction, such as "Dear Ms. Willis"?
- ❑ Does the cover letter include specific details about the writer's experience?
- ❑ Does the cover letter answer important questions?

Unit 5
- ❑ Does the paragraph describe how to use an app?
- ❑ Does the paragraph include each step in the process, from first to last?
- ❑ Does the paragraph include time-order words to introduce the steps?

Unit 6
- ❑ Does the paragraph compare and contrast two stores?
- ❑ Does the paragraph identify similarities between the stores?
- ❑ Does the paragraph identify differences between the stores?
- ❑ Does the paragraph include supporting details?

Unit 7
- ❑ Does the paragraph describe an accident?
- ❑ Does the paragraph present two opinions about who caused the accident?
- ❑ Does the paragraph clearly state an opinion and include reasons?

| Unit 8 | ❑ | Does the paragraph give an opinion about a food? |
| | ❑ | Does the paragraph support the opinion with facts? |

| Unit 9 | ❑ | Is the paragraph about a job and its duties? |
| | ❑ | Does the paragraph include and define new words or acronyms? |

Unit 10	❑	Does the paragraph end with a concluding sentence?
	❑	Does the concluding sentence summarize the paragraph or give an opinion?
	❑	Does the concluding sentence use a concluding word or phrase?

Unit 11	❑	Does the paragraph include different ways to save money?
	❑	Does the paragraph include specific examples?
	❑	Do the examples begin with *for example*, *such as*, or *for instance*?

| Unit 12 | ❑ | Does the paragraph describe a place? |
| | ❑ | Does the paragraph use sensory words to describe the place? |

Answer Key

UNIT 1

Page 2, Exercise A

1. i   6. f
2. g   7. a
3. d   8. h
4. b   9. c
5. e

Page 3, Exercise B

South America: Colombia, Ecuador, Argentina
Europe: Poland, Norway, Ukraine
Asia: the Philippines, Vietnam, Japan
Africa: Somalia, Algeria, Nigeria

Page 3, Exercise C

1. e   6. b
2. c   7. h
3. d   8. i
4. f   9. g
5. a

Page 4, Exercise A

1. doesn't live
2. have
3. doesn't play
4. has
5. don't watch
6. live
7. reminds
8. doesn't live

Page 4, Exercise B

1. What do you do in your free time?
2. How often does she go for a walk?
3. Where do they live now?
4. Do they live in Los Angeles?
5. Does he play American football?

Page 5, Exercise B

c

Page 5, Exercise C

b

Page 6, Exercise D

1. c. Line 2
2. b. Line 13
3. c. Line 24

Page 6, Exercise E

1. a   2. a   3. c

Page 6, Exercise F

1. a   2. a   3. b

Page 7, Exercise A

1. I rarely go to the movies.
2. Tim always goes to the park on Mondays
3. My sister never plays basketball after school.
4. We usually go to the supermarket on the weekend.
5. Sometimes I do exercises in the morning. / I sometimes do exercises in the morning.

Page 7, Exercise B

1. I always eat a big breakfast before I go to work.
2. I usually go to the library after school.
3. My children often shop at the mall on Sundays.
4. She sometimes meets her friends at a café after work.
5. I never eat before I go to bed.

Page 8, Exercise C

1. I often go to the pharmacy to pick up my medication.
2. My wife always goes to the post office to buy stamps.
3. My children usually play tennis on the weekend.
4. We never go to the hair salon during the week.
5. I rarely have a sandwich and fruit for lunch.

Page 8, Exercise D

Asha is from Somalia but now she lives in Minnesota. She and her family _usually_ eat dinner together. In Somalia, lunch was _always_ the biggest meal, but in the United States, families don't have time for a long lunch. Asha _usually_ fries her food. She and her family prefer lamb, but they don't _always_ get it. Sometimes they have beef or chicken. They also often have bread with their meals. They _always_ finish the meal with spicy sweet tea. In the United States, she is able to buy many kinds of vegetables. In Somalia, there weren't as many vegetables available so they _rarely_ had them.

Page 9, Exercise A

Circle the following:
¼ pound chicken meat
1 head lettuce
½ pound pasta (macaroni)
4 large tomatoes
1 tablespoon vinegar
1 tablespoon oil
salt

Page 9, Exercise B

1. c   2. a   3. a   4. b

Page 10, Exercise D

1. b   2. b   3. c   4. a

Page 11, Exercise A

1. a little
2. a lot of
3. any
4. much
5. several

Page 11, Exercise B

1. any
2. a lot of
3. any
4. a lot of
5. some
6. several

Page 12, Exercise A

a, c

Page 12, Exercise B

b

Page 12, Exercise C

I _moved_ to New York from Brazil two years ago. The town I am from is very small, but New York is a very big city! I came here because my cousin live_s_ here. He _works_ in a restaurant. He helped me get a job there, too. I like working there. The work _is_ hard but my co-workers are very friendly. At first, I didn't have _any_ friends. Now I have many friends. _We always_ go to the movies on Saturday nights.

Page 13, Exercise A

b

Page 13, Exercise B

1, 2, 4

Page 13, Exercise C

a, b, d

UNIT 2

Page 14, Exercise A

1. citizenship classes
2. financial aid
3. a high school diploma
4. a certificate

Page 14, Exercise B

1. b   2. c   3. e
4. a   5. d

Page 15, Exercise C

1. a   2. b   3. c
4. a   5. a   6. c

Page 16, Exercise A

1. won't
2. won't

3. will
4. might
5. will
6. won't

Page 16, Exercise B

1. might
2. will OR might
3. will
4. will
5. won't
6. might

Page 17, Exercise A

c

Page 17, Exercise C

a

Page 18, Exercise D

1. a. Line 2
2. a. Line 8
3. c. Line 15
4. c. Line 23

Page 18, Exercise E

1. a   2. a   3. a

Page 19, Exercise A

1. am
2. is
3. is
4. Are
5. Are

Page 19, Exercise B

1. isn't
2. are
3. aren't
4. is
5. isn't
6. are

Page 20, Exercise C

1. are going to visit
2. is going to ask
3. am going to find out
4. are going to try

Page 20, Exercise D

Adam works in a factory. He works at night and takes English classes in the morning. He wants a new job. He _is_ going to talk to a job counselor at his adult school. He is also ~~go~~ _going_ to the library to read about different types of jobs. He wants to start his own business. Adam likes fixing cars, so in the future he ~~are~~ _is_ going to open an auto repair shop. But for now, he wants to get more experience as a mechanic. So, he is going _to_ apply for a job at an auto repair shop near his home. Adam's wife is also ~~go~~ _going_ to look for a job. She wants to open a child-care business in their home. But first she is ~~going to~~ getting a job at a day-care center.

Page 22, Exercise C

1. Lack of focus
2. Media distraction
3. Fear and anxiety
4. 75 percent
5. 104

Page 23, Exercise A

1. First, I'm going to work and study English.
2. Second, I will apply for a community college program in automobile servicing.
3. Then, I will work part-time and study full-time for one year.
4. Next, I will pass the automotive service exam and receive my certificate.
5. Finally, I will look for full-time work

Page 23, Exercise B

b

Page 23, Exercise C

My goal is to ~~became~~ _become_ a welder. First, I need to improve my English. This fall, I am going _to_ enroll in a six-month language course. Then, I will apply ~~at~~ _for_ a welding training program at a community college. Next, I will pass the test and start looking for work at a manufacturing company. I might ~~worked~~ _work_ under a licensed welder for two years to get experience. ~~Final~~ _Finally_, I will work for myself. My friend also works as a welder. I'll ~~to~~ meet him tomorrow to talk about how to start my own business.

Page 24, Exercise A

1. am helping
2. isn't volunteering OR is not volunteering
3. aren't staying OR are not staying
4. is painting
5. are helping
6. is interviewing

Page 24, Exercise B

1. When is he helping at the community center?
2. Is the community center offering classes for adults?
3. What is she doing tomorrow night?
4. Are you getting your degree soon?

Page 25, Exercise B

1, 3, 4.

Page 25, Exercise C

a, b, d, e

UNIT 3

Page 26, Exercise A

1. figure out
2. look up a word
3. go online
4. make up a test

Page 26, Exercise B

1. b   2. d   3. a   4. c

Page 27, Exercise C

1. go to a parent-teacher conference
2. hand in homework
3. go online, do research
4. go over homework
5. make up a test

Page 28, Exercise A

1. have to
2. have to
3. should
4. should

Page 28, Exercise B

1. A. Does, have to take
   B. does not
2. should talk
3. should study
4. A. Do, have to speak
   B. do not

Page 28, Exercise C

1. Should I take the English placement test?
2. Does my son/brother/husband have to register by/register before a certain date?

Page 30, Exercise C

a

Page 30, Exercise D

1. a. Line 5
2. b. Line 21
3. a. Line 24

Page 30, Exercise E

1. c   2. c   3. a

Page 30, Exercise F

1. b   2. a

Page 31, Exercise A

Many students think math and science are more useful subjects than languages. I don't believe this to be true. First, speaking a second language _helps you connect with more people_. Second, learning another language _makes you stand out from other workers_. Finally, knowing more than one language _is important for some government jobs_.

Page 31, Exercise B

1. It is important for all students to take a P.E. class.
2. First, it helps students stay fit and healthy.
3. Second, it makes students learn about teamwork.
4. Finally, it is a great way to reduce stress.

Page 31, Exercise C

Martin want_s_ to go to a community college when he graduates high school. His school counselor says he has to take three year_s_ of English and social studies. He needs to study two years of math, science_,_ and P.E. He has _to_ take one year of _S_panish. He should also choose electives in subjects like life skills and music. He should think carefully about what course he would like to take in college. He _doesn't have to_ worry about choosing a major now. He has his school counselor to help him.

Page 32, Exercise A

1. It's very important to hand in homework on time.
2. It's a good idea to be punctual all the time.
3. It's sometimes difficult to remember new information.
4. It's often necessary to study hard before a test.

Page 32, Exercise B

1. It's important to sleep
2. It's a good idea to leave
3. It's a good idea for you to arrive
4. It's difficult to ask

Page 33, Exercise A

1. F   2. F   3. T
4. F   5. T   6. F

Page 34, Exercise B

1. c   2. c   3. b   4. b

Page 35, Exercise A

1. was
2. came
3. told
4. was
5. did not play/didn't play
6. did not pass/didn't pass
7. told
8. talked
9. did

Page 35, Exercise B

1. happened
2. told
3. Did
4. did not/didn't
5. called

Page 35, Exercise C

1. Alex hit Yonas in the playground.
2. Gerda wrote a mean note about another girl.
3. Susan stole Tom's pencil.
4. Ricardo said mean things about Kelly.

Page 36, Exercise D

1. b   2. a   3. d   4. e
5. c   6. g   7. h

Page 36, Exercise E

Yesterday Mrs. Leka ~~get~~ _got_ a phone call from the principal. He ~~says~~ _said_ that a boy in Vasil's class threatened him. The boy, Bill, ~~calling~~ _called_ Vasil names. Bill also ~~want~~ _wanted_ to fight Vasil after school. Fortunately, Vasil told his teacher. And the teacher ~~telling~~ _told_ the principal. Bill ~~is~~ _was_ suspended for one day.

Page 37, Exercice A

c

Page 37, Exercice B

1, 3

Page 37, Exercise C

a, b, c, d

UNIT 4

Page 38, Exercise A

1. motivated
2. punctual
3. efficient
4. organized

Page 38, Exercise B

1. c 2. d 3. a 4. e 5. b

Page 39, Exercise C

1. punctual
2. cooperative
3. organized
4. pleasant

Page 39, Exercise D

1. pleasant
2. organized
3. cooperative
4. dependable

Page 40, Exercise A

1. driven
2. worked
3. cooked
4. done
5. taken

Page 40, Exercise B

1. A: <u>Have you ever volunteered in your community?</u>
   B: Yes, I <u>have</u>.
2. A: <u>Has she ever served customers in a restaurant?</u>
   B: No, she <u>hasn't</u>.
3. A: <u>Have they ever used email for work?</u>
   B: Yes, they <u>have</u>.
4. A: <u>Has he ever worked for a large company?</u>
   B: No, he <u>hasn't</u>.

Page 41, Exercise A

Circle the following:
Helped open and close restaurant on Sundays, set up, served customers

Page 41, Exercise B

1. T
2. T
3. F: Carlos started as a cleaner.
4. F: Carlos started working in in August 2017.
5. F: Carlos left because the restaurant closed.
6. F: Carolos wants employers to call Pablo Sanchez for a reference.

Page 43, Exercise A

1. T   2. F   3. T   4. T

Page 43, Exercise B

1. for
2. since
3. for
4. for

Page 43, Exercise C

1. has volunteered
2. has had
3. has been
4. have served

Page 44, Exercise D

Answers will vary.
1. He has worked at Big Olly's Tires since 2014.
2. He has been Assistant Manager since 2017.
3. He has taught teenagers how to repair cars since 2014.
4. He has had his ASE Certification since 2014.

Page 45, Exercise B

b

Page 46, Exercise C

c

Page 46, Exercise D

1. a. Line 4
2. b. Line 8
3. c. Line 11
4. a. Line 21

Page 46, Exercise E

1. a   2. a   3. b   4. b

Page 47, Exercise A

1. c   2. e   3. d   4. a   5. b

Page 47, Exercise B

d

Page 47, Exercise C

I am writing to *apply* for the position of electrician at Energy Electric Co. I am qualified for this position because I am a licensed electrician and have experience in this area. I worked for an electrical services company in *Turkey for* two years before I moved to the U.S. in 2015. Since then, I have *worked* under a licensed electrician and have received a certificate in electrical engineering. Finally, I am *hardworking* and dependable, and I am motivated to do well in this job.

Page 48, Exercise A

1. I used to play soccer.
2. Olga used to go dancing.
3. Mr. and Mrs. Garcia used to live in Mexico.
4. He used to play chess.
5. Ting used to play the guitar.

Page 48, Exercise B

1. used to do
2. used to walk
3. used to play
4. used to listen
5. used to swim
6. used to have

Page 48, Exercise C

1. Royce <u>used to play</u> basketball every Friday.
2. Edwina and Julia <u>used to go</u> the beach on Sundays.
3. Trung <u>used to go</u> to the farmers market in the morning.
4. Marta <u>used to eat</u> her biggest meal at lunch.

Page 49, Exercise A

c

Page 49, Exercise B

1, 2, 3

Page 49, Exercise C

a, b, d

UNIT 5

Page 50, Exercise A

1. ticket agent
2. arrivals and departures display
3. X-ray machine
4. boarding pass
5. carry-on bag
6. passenger

Page 50, Exercise B

1. e   2. c   3. d   4. a   5. b

Page 51, Exercise C

1. a   2. b   3. b   4. a   5. c

Page 51, Exercise D

Person: passenger, ticket agent, security agent
Place: gate, kiosk
Thing: metal detector, luggage, e-ticket,

Page 52, Exercise A

1. couldn't
2. can't
3. can
4. were
5. couldn't
6. weren't
7. will
8. couldn't
9. won't
10. wasn't

Page 52, Exercise B

1. couldn't
2. can't, can
3. was able to

Page 53, Exercise A

Circle: TERMINAL, CURBSIDE CHECK-IN

Page 53, Exercise B

1. b   2. b   3. c   4. a   5. a

Page 54, Exercise C

1. b   2. c   3. a

Page 54, Exercise D

1. T   2. F   3. T   4. F

Page 55, Exercise A

1. their
2. Hers
3. my
4. Your
5. yours
6. mine

Page 55, Exercise B

1. Hers
2. mine
3. theirs
4. hers
5. his
6. mine

Page 56, Exercise C

1. is
2. is
3. are
4. is
5. is

Page 56, Exercise D

1. his
2. her
3. ours
4. his
5. A: my
   B: your
   A: mine

Page 57, Exercise B

b

Page 58, Exercise C

a

Page 58, Exercise D

1. b. Line 9
2. c. Line 21
3. a. Line 24

Page 58, Exercise E

1. a   2. b

Page 58, Exercise F

1. a   2. b   3. a

Page 59, Exercise A

1. First, find the bike-share company's website or app.
2. Second, create an account.
3. Then, use the bike-share map to find the nearest bike station to your location.
4. Next, go to the bike station and type in your account number to pick up a bike.
5. After that, use your map to find the nearest bike station to your destination.
6. Finally, cycle to the other bike station and leave your bike there.

Page 59, Exercise B

1. First
2. Second
3. Then
4. Next
5. Finally

Page 59, Exercise C

This is how to use a map app to get to your destination quickly. _First_, tap on the map app on _your_ phone. It will show _your_ current location. Next, type in where you want to go and tap on the directions button. _After that_, the app will show you different ways of getting to your destination, such as by driving, using public transportation, cycling, or walking. Finally, you _can_ choose the quickest option by comparing the different lengths of time.

Page 60, Exercise A

1. Could you tell me the time?
2. Will you get me a soda?
3. Would you help me with my bags?
4. Could you check the train schedule for me?
5. Can you tell me when the bus will arrive?

Page 60, Exercise B

1. Yes, you can.
2. Yes, you can.
3. No, you can't.
4. Yes, you can.
5. Sorry. No, you can't.
6. No, I'm sorry, you can't.

Page 61, Exercise A

b

Page 61, Exercise B

1, 2, 4

Page 61, Exercise C

a, b, c, e

UNIT 6

Page 62, Exercise A

1. dented
2. damaged OR broken OR defective
3. incompatible
4. leaking
5. bent
6. broken OR damaged OR defective
7. cracked
8. defective OR broken OR damaged

Page 63, Exercise B

1. incompatible
2. scratched
3. leaking
4. dented
5. cracked
6. defective

Page 64, Exercise A

1. The phone is broken, and the vacuum cleaner is, too.
2. My tablet is scratched, and my computer screen is scratched, too.
3. Her camera isn't working, and her LED TV isn't working, either.
4. Delivery is free, and repairs are free, too.
5. The treadmill isn't covered under the warranty, and the microwave isn't covered under the warranty, either.

Page 64, Exercise B

Answers will vary.
1. The coffeemaker is leaking, and the faucet is, too.
2. The refrigerator is not working and is not covered under warranty.
3. The charger is not compatible with my phone.
4. The air conditioner is not working, and the refrigerator is broken, too.
5. The treadmill is damaged, and the washing machine is, too.
6. The washing machine is dented, and the refrigerator is damaged, too.

Page 65, Exercise A

b

Page 65, Exercise C

a

Page 66, Exercise D

1. a. Line 9
2. b. Line 16
3. c. Line 22

Page 66, Exercise E

1. a   2. a   3. b

Page 66, Exercise F

1. a   2. b   3. a

Page 67, Exercise A

1. T   2. F   3. T   4. T

Page 67, Exercise B

1. is safer
2. is smaller
3. is less expensive
4. is heavier
5. is more difficult

Page 68, Exercise C

1. lower
2. more convenient

3. better
4. happier

Page 68, Exercise D

1. The Sun Wave is bigger than the Thermos 2000.
2. The Sun Wave is more efficient than the Thermos 2000.
3. The Thermos 2000 is smaller than the Sun Wave.
4. The Thermos 2000 is cheaper than the Sun Wave.

Page 69, Exercise A

1. T   2. F   3. F   4. T   5. F

Page 70, Exercise A

1. as close as
2. not as low as
3. not as dependable as
4. not as convenient as
5. as good as

Page 70, Exercise B

1. is not as heavy as
2. is not as expensive as
3. is not as cheap as
4. is not as easy to carry as

Page 71, Exercise C

1. Bee's customer service is not as good as Abe's.
2. Bee's prices are not as high as Abe's.
3. Bee's location is not as convenient as Abe's.
4. Bee's store hours are not as good as Abe's.
5. Abe's selection is not as wide as Bee's.

Page 71, Exercise D

1. The Viza is not as expensive as the Polara.
2. The Viza is not as big as the Polara.
3. The Viza is not as fast as the Polara.

Page 72, Exercise A

1. F   2. T   3. F

Page 72, Exercise B

1. c   2. b

Page 72, Exercise C

E-Buy and LectroWorld are two electronic stores in my city. Each *store* has a well-organized website where you can check the latest offers. There is also a good selection of appliances at both stores, *too*. However, I prefer to buy my appliances at E-Buy. The rebates at E-Buy are usually *better*, and the delivery charges are *cheaper*, too. The customer service at LectroWorld isn't *as* good as E-Buy. The store doesn't offer free returns, *either*.

Page 73, Exercise A

a

Page 73, Exercise B

1, 2, 3

Page 73, Exercise C

a, b, d

UNIT 7

Page 74, Exercise A

1. construction
2. highway
3. traffic jam
4. tow truck
5. toll booth
6. vehicle

Page 74, Exercise B

1. overpass
2. construction
3. traffic jam
4. lanes
5. exit

Page 75, Exercise C

1. b 2. a 3. a 4. c 5. c

Page 76, Exercise A

1. an
2. a
3. the
4. The
5. a
6. The

Page 76, Exercise B

1. an
2. a
3. a
4. an
5. the
6. the

Page 76, Exercise C

1. You need to replace the brakes.
2. Your car has an oil leak.
3. You need to clean the air filter.
4. You need to change the fan belt.
5. You need to get a new tire.

Page 77, Exercise A

1. hood
2. windshield
3. sideview mirror
4. trunk
5. headlights
6. engine

Page 77, Exercise B

1. windshield
2. engine
3. trunk
4. headlights
5. windshield
6. hood

Page 78, Exercise C

1. brake pedal
2. horn
3. glove compartment
4. GPS
5. accelerator/gas pedal
6. rearview mirror

Page 78, Exercise D

1. GPS
2. accelerator/gas pedal
3. rearview mirror
4. brakes

Page 79, Exercise A

1. The man was talking on a cell phone.
2. The drivers were watching the road.
3. The passengers weren't wearing seatbelts.

Page 79, Exercise B

1. was watching
2. were interviewing
3. were waiting
4. was sitting
5. was not paying attention

Page 79, Exercise C

1. The driver was eating and drinking.
2. The man was using his cell phone.
3. The woman was putting on makeup.

Page 80, Exercise D

1. was waiting
2. was talking
3. was wearing
4. was wearing
5. was running
6. was planning

Page 80, Exercise E

1. I was sitting in my car.
2. The radio was playing.
3. My cell phone was ringing.
4. The mechanics were fixing my car.
5. You were looking at the rearview mirror.

Page 81, Exercise A

a

Page 82, Exercise C

a

Page 82, Exercise D

1. b. Line 6
2. a. Line 18
3. a. Line 19

Page 82, Exercise E

1. a   2. b   3. b

Page 82, Exercise F

1. a   2. b   3. b

Page 83, Exercise A

Taxi driver's opinion: The crash is the SUV driver's fault.
Supporting sentence: He said: "Your car is parked too far out into the road!"
SUV driver's opinion: The crash is the taxi driver's fault.
Supporting sentence: He said: "I parked correctly! Look! My car is close to the line."

Page 83, Exercise B

1. c   2. a   3. b

Circle: 2

Page 83, Exercise C

Traffic was slow _on_ the way to work this morning. Drivers were getting impatient. A hybrid _crashed_ into the sedan in front of it. The woman driving _the_ hybrid said, "You need to move off more quickly!" The man in the sedan _said_, "You _weren't_ paying attention! You need to wait for my car to move before you drive." I think the driver of the hybrid was at fault.

When she got out of the car, she
was _rubbing_ her eyes. I think she
was too tired to concentrate on
driving.

Page 84, Exercise A

1. e 2. d 3. a 4. b 5. c

Page 84, Exercise B

1. When you buy a car, you need
   to have insurance. OR You need
   to have insurance when you
   buy a car.
2. Before you sign the contract,
   you need to understand all
   the costs. OR You need to
   understand all the costs before
   you sign the contract.
3. Your car loses value when
   you drive it home from the car
   dealership. OR When you drive
   it home from the dealership,
   your car loses value.
4. You need to look out for
   pedestrians when you drive
   in town. OR When you drive in
   town, you need to look out for
   pedestrians.

Page 84, Exercise C

1. When you drive, look around to
   be safe.
2. Before you turn, check that no
   one is in your way.
3. Before you change lanes, look
   over your shoulder.
4. After you get in a car, put on a
   seat belt.
5. When you buy insurance,
   you need to understand the
   coverage.

Page 85, Exercise A

b

Page 85, Exercise B

1, 2

Page 85, Exercise C

a, c, d, e

UNIT 8

Page 86, Exercise A

1. e   2. f   3. d
4. a   5. c   6. b

Page 86, Exercise B

1. have a snack
2. drink sugary beverages
3. buy fresh fruits and vegetables
4. cook homemade meals

Page 87, Exercise C

1. fast food
2. takeout
3. cook homemade meals
4. buy fresh fruits and vegetables
5. sugary
6. frozen dinners

Page 88, Exercise A

1. quickest
2. busiest
3. hardest
4. most interesting
5. happiest

Page 88, Exercise B

1. the fastest
2. the most expensive
3. the most difficult
4. the best
5. the healthiest
6. most delicious

Page 89, Exercise A

1. 2, 0.5
2. Spring Valley Peanut
3. Yogurt Protein, Spring Valley
   Peanut
4. 13, 11
5. 2

Page 91, Exercise B

1. Neither
2. Spring Valley Peanut Bar
3. Neither
4. Yogurt Protein Bar
5. Neither

Page 91, Exercise A

1. They like eating candy bars at
   the movies. OR At the movies,
   they like eating candy bars.
2. He enjoys drinking juice in the
   morning. OR In the morning, he
   enjoys drinking juice.
3. She doesn't mind waking up
   early.
4. We like playing basketball after
   work. OR After work, we like
   playing basketball.
5. We enjoy eating takeout on
   the weekends. OR On the
   weekends, we enjoy eating
   takeout.

Page 91, Exercise B

1. doing
2. drinking
3. eating
4. dieting
5. taking
6. vacuuming

Page 92, Exercise C

1. stop eating
2. start exercising
3. doesn't enjoy running
4. doesn't like swimming
5. doesn't mind going
6. spend time planning

Page 92, Exercise D

Answers will vary.

1. Think about cooking smaller
   meals.
2. Consider giving them fruits and
   vegetables for a snack.
3. Try cooking homemade meals
   more often.
4. Try increasing their physical
   activity.

Page 93, Exercise B

a

Page 94, Exercise C

b

Page 94, Exercise D

1. b. Line 14
2. a. Line 22
3. c. Line 25

Page 94, Exercise E

1. c   2. b   3. a

Page 94, Exercise F

1. a   2. a   3. b

Page 95, Exercise A

1. Going to the dentist can be scary for young children.
2. Flossing your teeth regularly is good for your dental health.
3. Brushing after every meal is important.
4. Eating sugary food is not good for teeth.
5. Drinking milk can help keep your teeth strong.

Page 95, Exercise B

1. Seeing your dentist at least twice a year is a good idea.
2. Flossing every night before bed is important.
3. Flossing every day is hard to remember. **OR** Remembering to floss every day is hard.
4. Drinking a lot of sugary beverages is bad for your teeth.
5. Going to the dentist is a good idea if you feel any pain in your teeth or gums.

Page 96, Exercise A

a

Page 96, Exercise B

1. F   2. T   3. T   4. F

Page 96, Exercise C

Being on a diet can be difficult. One of the _best_ ways to change

your diet is to have healthy substitutes of the things you like to eat and drink. For example, if you like whole fat milk, _try_ drinking low-fat milk instead. _Avoiding_ fast food and takeout is also important. If you like Chinese food, think about _cooking_ it yourself. There are lots of different recipes online. If you don't have much time, look for the _quickest_ recipe you can cook.

Page 97, Exercise A

b

Page 97, Exercise B

1, 2, 4

Page 97, Exercise C

b, d, e

UNIT 9

Page 98, Exercise A

1. b   2. d   3. a   4. c

Page 98, Exercise B

1. b   2. c   3. b   4. a

Page 99, Exercise C

1. train other employees
2. attend a training session
3. be part of a team
4. deal with complaints

Page 99, Exercise D

1. train other employees
2. deal with complaints
3. attend a training session
4. be part of a team

Page 100, Exercise A

1. one
2. ones
3. one
4. one
5. ones

Page 100, Exercise B

1. one
2. one
3. one
4. ones
5. one

Page 100, Exercise C

A: Hi. Can I see that camera?
B: Which ~~ones~~ _one_?
A: ~~Those~~ _That_ one. The silver ~~ones~~ _one_.
B: Here you go.
A: It's nice. How much is it?
B: For that one? It's $129.99.
A: Hmm. Do you have a cheaper one?
B: Yes. In that case over there we have a discounted ~~ones~~ _one_.

Page 101, Exercise A

b

Page 102, Exercise C

a

Page 102, Exercise D

1. b. Line 8
2. a. Line 14
3. c. Line 26

Page 102, Exercise E

1. a   2. a

Page 102, Exercise F

1. a   2. b   3. a

Page 103, Exercise A

1. c   2. a   3. d   4. b

Page 103, Exercise B

1. b

Page 103, Exercise C

If someone has a serious accident or is very sick, they are sometimes sent to an ICU (intensive care unit) in a hospital. In an IC*U*, doctors and nurses can watch the sick or injured person very closely. They can give the person different types of treatments. Some treatments might not work, but other one*s* might. If the person gets worse, they may also be sent to an <u>OR</u>. This refer*s* to the operating room where doctors perform certain medical procedures.

Page 104, Exercise A

1. F   2. F   3. T   4. F

Page 104, Exercise B

1. Sandra needs you to close the store.
2. Do you want me to come early?
3. Does she expect me to finish before 5:00?
4. The manager would like his employee to apologize to a customer.
5. The manager expects us to clean our work area.

Page 105, Exercise C

1. all employees to follow the rules at all times
2. all employees to be at work five minutes before their shift starts
3. them to be friendly to customers and provide excellent customer service
4. his boss to know he's an excellent worker

Page 105, Exercise D

Answers will vary.
1. Management requires employees to wash their hands after using the restroom.
2. Management requires employees to keep their work area clean at all times.

3. Management requires employees to tell their supervisor when an accident happens.
4. Management requires employees to wear eye protection when operating any equipment.

Page 106, Exercise A

If an employee has a back injury, do not move him or her. Wait for medical attention from authorized personal.

Page 106, Exercise B

1. F   2. F   3. F   4. T   5. F

Page 107, Exercise C

1. c   2. b   3. d   4. a

Page 107, Exercise D

1. Wear safety boots
2. Wear ear protection
3. Hot surface: Do not touch
4. Watch for forklifts
5. Wear goggles
6. Caution: Trip hazard

Page 108, Exercise A

1. The manager told Stefani to put the boxes in the storage closet.
2. The manager told Fred to sweep up the aisle.
3. The manager told Thomas not to open the store before 7:00.
4. The manager told Sandra to call the supplier and order more materials.

Page 108, Exercise B

Answers will vary.
The manager told the employees to put paper in the printers.
The manager asked the employees to unplug the copier at the end of the day.

The manager told the employees to keep the warehouse clean and organized.
The manager asked the employees to put the phones on "night mode" at the end of the day.
The manager told the employees to enter the security code and exit within 30 seconds when you leave.

Page 109, Exercise A

b

Page 109, Exercise B

1, 2, 3

Page 109, Exercise C

b, d, e

UNIT 10

Page 110, Exercise A

1. physical therapy
2. admissions
3. surgery
4. intensive care unit (ICU)
5. pediatrics
6. laboratory

Page 111, Exercise B

1. Admissions
2. Physical therapy
3. Surgery
4. Pediatrics
5. Laboratory

Page 111, Exercise C

1. radiology/imaging
2. intensive care unit (ICU)
3. emergency room (ER)
4. nurse's station
5. laboratory
6. maternity ward

Page 112, Exercise A

1. frustrating
2. tired
3. confused
4. tiring
5. frustrated
6. confusing

Page 112, Exercise B

1. confused
2. embarrassing
3. frustrating
4. interested
5. frightening
6. tired

Page 113, Exercise C

1. scared
2. frightening
3. satisfied
4. excited
5. worried
6. interesting

Page 113, Exercise D

1. They feel scared.
2. No. They are confusing.
3. They feel embarrassed.
4. He feels relieved.
5. It is frustrating.
6. They feel stressed.

Page 114, Exercise A

1. b 2. a 3. a 4. a 5. b

Page 115, Exercise C

Answers will vary.
Ms. Kim was complaining of stomach pain.
She has had these symptoms for three days.
Yes. She was under the care of Dr. Lin last year for stomach pain.

Page 116, Exercise A

1. My uncle has been having bad headaches for three days.
2. My aunt has been coughing for two weeks.
3. My husband has not been sleeping well.
4. I have not been eating well.
5. My daughter has been complaining about back pains.

Page 116, Exercise B

Mr. Cruz: I've been having OR I have been having
Dr. Patel: Have you been taking
Mr. Cruz: I have been taking OR I've been taking
Dr. Patel: Have you been smoking
Mr. Cruz: I haven't been smoking OR I have not been smoking

Page 117, Exercise A

c

Page 117, Exercise C

b

Page 118, Exercise D

1. a. Line 9
2. b. Line 20
3. c. Line 24

Page 118, Exercise E

1. c   2. a   3. b

Page 118, Exercise F

1. b   2. a   3. a   4. a

Page 119, Exercise A

b

Page 119, Exercise B

2

Page 119, Exercise C

I think sleep is _an_ important part of a healthy lifestyle. It allows your body to rest and recover. It also gives you lots _of_ energy. I have been _trying_ to form good sleep habits for years. First, I turn off all screens one hour before bed. Then, I listen to music to relax. Finally, I have a cup of warm milk. Most nights I sleep for seven hours. It's very _frustrating_ when I don't sleep well. I wake up _tired_. In conclusion, I think more people should form good sleep habits.

Page 120, Exercise A

1. missing
2. paying
3. losing
4. falling

Page 120, Exercise B

If people are serious ~~of~~ _about_ taking care of their health, they should pay attention to their cholesterol levels. Many people are worried _about_ getting high cholesterol. What is it and why are people concerned ~~for~~ _about_ getting it? High blood cholesterol increases the risk of heart disease or stroke. Saturated fats in foods like red meat and eggs increase cholesterol levels. Smokers are also at risk for high cholesterol. People with high cholesterol usually don't have any symptoms. However, sometimes they may complain ~~of~~ _about_ feeling dizzy. Controlling cholesterol is important. People who want to lower their cholesterol should think ~~to~~ _about_ quitting smoking. They also need to eat a diet with less saturated fat, and they should exercise. It is also important to have your cholesterol checked regularly.

Page 121, Exercise A

c

Page 121, Exercise B

1, 2, 3

Page 121, Exercise C

b, c, d, e

UNIT 11

Page 122, Exercise A

1. ATM withdrawal
2. ATM/debit card
3. credit card
4. check
5. bank teller
6. bank statement

Page 123, Exercise B

1. b   2. a   3. c   4. a

Page 123, Exercise C

1. balance
2. credit card
3. bank teller
4. withdrawal
5. check
6. bank statement

Page 124, Exercise A

1. If you don't pay your credit card bill on time, you may have to pay a large fee. **OR** You may have to pay a large fee if you don't pay your credit card bill on time.
2. If you pay your bills online, you can save time and money on stamps. **OR** You can save time and money on stamps if you pay your bills online.
3. If you open an online savings account, you can get a high interest rate. **OR** You can get a high interest rate if you open an online savings account.
4. If you lose your credit card, call the credit card company immediately. **OR** Call the credit card company immediately if you lose your credit card.

5. If you change your PIN often, you can keep your account safe. **OR** You can keep your account safe if you change your PIN often.

Page 124, Exercise B

Answers will vary.

1. You can get free checking if you open an account online.
2. You can get free checks for 12 months if you open an account this month.
3. You can get a free ATM/Debit card if you open an account.
4. You can get a $50 cash bonus if your new account is open for six months.
5. You can get customer support 24/7 if you are an online customer.

Page 125, Exercise B

b

Page 126, Exercise C

a

Page 126, Exercise D

1. b. Line 19
2. a. Line 12
3. b. Line 19

Page 126, Exercise E

1. b   2. a   3. b

Page 126, Exercise F

1. a   2. a   3. a

Page 127, Exercise A

1, 3

Page 127, Exercise B

1. c   2. a   3. b

Page 127, Exercise C

In addition to utility bills, cell phone bills can sometimes be expensive. However, there *are* ways to reduce these bills. *For example*, you could change your cell phone carrier. If you compare different plans online, you can usually find a good deal. Check out what is included in each plan, such *as* talk, text, and *data* per month. Some cell phone services also offer special discounts. For *instance*, if you call a certain country very often, some services offer a lower rate to call that country.

Page 128, Exercise A

1. might find
2. follow
3. offer
4. shop
5. get

Page 128, Exercise B

1. If you check the newspaper, you will find good deals on rentals **OR** might find good deals on rentals.
2. If you get insurance for your home, you will be able to protect your things.
3. Their electric bill will go down if they keep the heating low.
4. You will save money **OR** might save money if you learn to do small repairs yourself.
5. If you fix leaks around your windows, you will **OR** might save money on heating and cooling.
6. If you sign a long-term lease, you will **OR** might save on your rent.

Page 129, Exercise A

Circle: $147.38

Page 130, Exercise B

1. F   2. T   3. F
4. T   5. F   6. F

Page 130, Exercise C

1. a   2. b   3. b   4. a

Page 131, Exercise A

1. I don't mind renting a room.
2. We prefer to live near the city.
3. She loves living close to work.
4. The manager promised to see us.
5. They finished painting the living room.
6. We need to pay all utilities.

Page 131, Exercise B

1. to live
2. talking
3. looking
4. to wait
5. to move
6. living

Page 132, Exercise C

1. living
2. to have
3. looking
4. unpacking

Page 133, Exercise A

a

Page 133, Exercise B

2, 3, 4

Page 133, Exercise C

a, b, c

UNIT 12

Page 134, Exercise A

1. a   2. b   3. c   4. d
5. e   6. f   7. h   8. g

Page 135, Exercise B

1. b   2. c   3. a   4. a   5. b

Page 135, Exercise C

1. Pentagon
2. Smithsonian Institution
3. Capitol Building
4. Washington Monument
5. White House

Page 136, Exercise A

1. does
2. don't
3. didn't
4. did
5. doesn't
6. didn't
7. do

Page 136, Exercise B

1. My grandmother lives in Dallas, and my aunt and cousins do, too.
2. We take the subway to school, and our neighbor does, too.
3. You don't want to miss the tour of the Oval Office, and I don't, either.
4. They go to the park after class each day, and their friends do, too.
5. His parents like visiting the Smithsonian Institution, and he does, too.
6. I don't like to travel by bus, and she doesn't, either.
7. My father buys his museum tickets online, and my daughter does, too

Page 137, Exercise A

1. North
2. Blue
3. No
4. Three
5. East
6. Yellow, Green, and Red

Page 138, Exercise B

1. Green line
2. north
3. Red
4. east
5. two
6. north
7. Green line
8. Gallery Place
9. two

Page 139, Exercise A

1. New laws are signed by the President.
2. Laws are enforced by the Judiciary.
3. The U.S. Constitution is known as the supreme law of the land.
4. State senators are elected every six years.

Page 139, Exercise B

1. is visited
2. is named
3. are known
4. is seen

Page 139, Exercise C

1. Laws are created by Congress in the Capitol Building
2. The president of the United States is chosen every four years by registered voters.
3. Cabinet members are chosen by the president.
4. The U.S. military is controlled by the president.

Page 140, Exercise B

a

Page 141, Exercise C

b

Page 141, Exercise D

1. b. Line 9
2. c. Line 13
3. c. Line 24

Page 141, Exercise E

1. a   2. c   3. a

Page 141, Exercise F

1. a   2. a   3. a

Page 142, Exercise A

1. The location of Washington, D.C. was chosen by Alexander Hamilton.
2. Pierre L'Enfant was selected by President Washington to design Washington, D.C.
3. America's freedom was won by Washington's army.
4. The Declaration of Independence was written by Thomas Jefferson.

Page 142, Exercise B

1. was designed
2. was built
3. was burned down
4. were housed
5. was installed
6. were added

Page 143, Exercise C

1. were used
2. were established
3. was granted
4. was given
5. was not allowed
6. were seen
7. were replaced

Page 143, Exercise D

1. John Adams was elected as the second president of the U.S.
2. In the 1780s, money was created by each state.
3. In 1865, slavery was made illegal in the U.S.
4. The British were defeated in the War of Independence.

Page 144, Exercise A

Sight: bright, beautiful
Smell: salty, spiced
Sound: loud, happy
Taste: sweet, strong
Touch: icy, warm

Page 144, Exercise B

The iced tea at the café was not very good. There was not enough ice in it. I wanted something _cold_ to drink, but it was _warm_. It was also made with too much water and lemon. I like my tea to taste _strong_. Then I had to add more sugar because it tasted so _bitter_! I won't buy iced tea there again.

Page 144, Exercise C

I have some tips for your visit to _the_ museum next week! The sandwiches in the café _are_ good value and the soups are, _too_. The fries smell great. However, the portions aren't very large, and the salads _aren't_, either. People were complaining about the prices. The cakes are _located_ beside the cash desk. They taste really fresh. Be sure to try some herbal tea. The mint is grown in the museum garden. Look for a table upstairs. Lots of groups _were_ seated in the main dining area, and it was very noisy.

Page 145, Exercise A

a

Page 145, Exercise B

1, 3

Page 145, Exercise C

d, e

Notes

Credits

Illustration credits: Kenneth Batelman: p.53; Electra Graphics: pp. 14, 50 (4), 137; Stephen Hutchings: p. 43; Gary Torrisi: p. 67; Dataflow International: pp. 5, 9, 15, 17, 22, 29, 33, 34, 39, 41, 42, 44, 45, 47, 54, 57, 65, 69, 71, 80, 81, 87, 93, 101, 105, 106, 107, 108, 114, 115, 117, 124, 125, 129, 132, 140.

Photo Credits: Front cover: Golero/E+/Getty Images; Ariel Skelley/DigitalVision/Getty Images; Sam Edwards/Caiaimage/Getty Images. Page 13: Syda Productions/Shutterstock; 17: Maskot/Getty Images; 25: Atic12/123RF; 26 (1): Tom Wang/Shutterstock; 26 (2): Franck Boston/Shutterstock; 26 (3): Ian Shaw/Alamy Stock Photo; 26 (4): Fuse/Corbis/Getty Images; 37: Asiseeit/E+/Getty Images; 38 (1): Dynamic Graphics/Creatas/Getty Images; 38 (2): Fuse/Corbis/Getty Images; 38 (3): Erik Isakson/Getty Images; 38 (4): Stuart Forster/Alamy Stock Photo; 45: PeopleImages/E+/Getty Images; 49: Sidekick/E+/Getty Images; 50 (1): Simon Marcus Taplin/Corbis/Getty Images; 50 (2): Hans Blossey/imageBROKER/Getty Images; 50 (3): Baona/E+/Getty Images; 50 (5): Asiseeit/E+/Getty Images; 50 (6): Amble Design/Shutterstock; 60: Cathy Yeulet/123RF; 61: Shutterstock; 62 (1): Tom Gril/Photographer's Choice RF/Getty Images; 62 (2): LightField Studios/Shutterstock; 62 (3): Santi Nanta/Shutterstock; 62 (4): NET_Photog/Shutterstock; 62 (5): Roman Demkiv/Shutterstock; 62 (6): Maxim Mayorov/Shutterstock; 62 (7): Andrey_Popov/Shutterstock; 62 (8): Stock-Asso/Shutterstock; 63 (1): Mikroman6/Moment/Getty Images; 63 (2): Claudio Divizia/Shutterstock; 63 (3): LisaValder/E+/Getty Images; 63 (4): Bgwalker/E+/Getty Images; 63 (5): Patrick Strattner/Getty Images; 63 (6): Daniel Grizelj/Stone/Getty Images; 68 (left): Aquarius Studio/Shutterstock; 68 (right): Arka38/Shutterstock; 69: Oleksiy Mark/Shutterstock; 70 (left): i studio/Alamy Stock Photo; 70 (right): Hurst Photo/Shutterstock; 71 (left): Africa Studio/Shutterstock; 71 (right): Chakrapong Worathat/123RF; 73: EXTREME-PHOTOGRAPHER/E+/Getty Images; 74 (1): SteveDF/E+/Getty Images; 74 (2): Lightpoet/Shutterstock; 74 (3): Burwellphotography/E+/Getty Images; 74 (4): CrispyPork/Shutterstock; 74 (5): John Greim/LightRocket/Getty Images; 74 (6): Arand/E+/Getty Images 77: Alex Maxim/123RF; 78: Algre/123RF; 79 (left): Brigitte Sporrer/Corbis/Getty Images; 79 (center): Antonio Diaz/123RF; 79 (right): Andrey Armyagov/Shutterstock; 80: Tele52/Shutterstock; 85: Stuart Jenner/Shutterstock; 86 (a): Dinodia Photos/Alamy Stock Photo; 86 (b): Radius Images/Alamy Stock Photo; 86 (c): Jack Hollingsworth/Photodisc/Getty Images; 86 (d): Angela Hampton/Angela Hampton Picture Library/Alamy Stock Photo; 86 (e): Jasmin Merdan/Moment/Getty Images; 86 (f): Greg Vaughn/Alamy Stock Photo; 87: Ansonmiao/E+/Getty Images; 97: Pavel L Photo and Video/Shutterstock; 99 (1): Colorblind Images LLC/DigitalVision/Getty Images; 99 (2): Jeffbergen/E+/Getty Images; 99 (3): Shaunl/E+/Getty Images; 99 (4): Africa Studio/Shutterstock; 109: Shutterstock; 110 (1): Africa Studio/Shutterstock; 110 (2): Dean Mitchell/E+/Getty Images; 110 (3): Levent Konuk/Shutterstock 110 (4): Tyler Olson/123RF; 110 (5): Fuse/Corbis/Getty Images; 110 (6): BSIP/Universal Images Group Editorial/Getty Images; 122 (1): Sanjagrujic/Shutterstock; 122 (2): Rtimages/Shutterstock; 122 (3): Slaven/Shutterstock; 122 (5): YinYang/E+/Getty Images; 122 (6): Tele52/Shutterstock; 133: Wavebreakmedia/Shutterstock; 134 (a): Travel Bug/Shutterstock; 134 (b): MDOGAN/Shutterstock; 134 (c): Orhan Cam/Shutterstock; 134 (d): Ivan Cholakov/Shutterstock 134 (e): Orhan Cam/Shutterstock; 134 (f): Michael G Smith/Shutterstock; 134 (g): Orhan Cam/Shuttertsock; 134 (h): © www.stefanbock.de/Moment/Getty Images; 145: Stokkete/Shutterstock.